Story of Giant
PANDA
Tan Kai

China Intercontinental Press

CONTENTS

PREFACE

People around the world today love giant pandas, perhaps little realizing that the ancient people of China were already familiar with the animal. In famous ancient books, it was successively referred to as "Pi" (a mythical bearlike wild animal), "Pi Xiu" (ditto), "Mo", "Tapir", "Iron-eating Beast" and "White Leopard", and so on. The giant panda is a combination of white and black fur, and these colors can be said to symbolize Chinese culture. From the Tai Chi diagram with the interlacement of black and white to "Hetu" and "Luoshu" with the arrangement of white and black dotted lines, and from the board used to play *Go (Weiqi)* with its black and white squares to Chinese paintings with their infinite charm created by black ink and white paper, all of these show the essence of Chinese culture. This can be summed up in expressions such as "profound truth is the most simple and easiest to grasp" embodying rich philosophical connotations – "be both opposite and complementary (to each other)" and "critical thoughts in plain and simple matters". It seems that the giant panda is born to naturally inherit the characteristics of Chinese culture and become the animal that can best embody them.

The giant panda has captured the hearts of countless Chinese and foreign "fans" for its austere and cute appearance. People's love for panda transcends geographical boundaries, races and ideology, becoming the embodiment of the great love most treasured by humans.

As an ancient relic animal, it is regarded as a "national treasure" by the Chinese people, while the World Wildlife Fund (WWF) takes it as a symbol of global nature protection.

Thanks to the joint efforts of several generations of Chinese and international protection workers, considerable progress has been made in giant panda conservation. Construction of nature reserves is well underway to effectively protect the small population of giant pandas; rescue projects have been implemented to better facilitate protection of the panda's habitat; national surveys are carried out continuously to provide first-hand information for ensuring the animal's conservation; giant panda ex-situ conservation has been conducted; when the captive panda population reaches a certain scale, animals are released back into nature as part of a positive interaction between ex-situ conservation and in-situ conservation. Currently, the population of wild panda is described as "steadily rising", which is really gratifying.

Many people today are eager to know more about the secret life and little-known stories of giant pandas. However, how to make "hard lumps" of scientific knowledge blend into "digestible" literature has long posed difficulties.

However, when I met Mr. Tan Kai, I appreciated and admired him for his attitude of feeling at ease with both science and the humanities and the spirit of sharing knowledge with the public through a down-to-earth approach.

As a veteran in the field of literature and science, Tan Kai served as chief editor of *Science Fiction World* for 24 years and helped it become a popular periodical in China and the world's largest-circulation science fiction magazine. He continues his work of discovery and enthusiastically supports a large number of today's popular science fiction writers. Besides text editing, Tan Kai also adheres to scientific, literary and artistic creation. In this spirit, he has made frequent journeys to China's panda reserves and has written a number of popular science works, scientific poems and literature reports related to the giant panda.

Wu Xiankui, director of the Sichuan Science Writers Association, delivered a keynote speech entitled "Three Primary Colors in Tan Kai's Life". These, he said, were "passion, pandas and science". "I believe that is really a true portrayal of Tan Kai's life," Wu said.

Tan Kai has been engaged in panda protection for 34 years ago. His *Story of Giant Panda* can be regarded as another masterpiece that sum up his work in this field. Through vivid and interesting stories, the book details the history and the origin of the panda, panda's habits, release process and the moving stories of interaction between pandas and humans. Scientific knowledge is organically associated with people's panda emotions in this work in an incisive and vivid way. I think this book will gain many Chinese and foreign readers.

I wish that *Story of Giant Panda* can become an exquisite gift book and Chinese culture about giant pandas can spread to the world as a whole!

Hu Jinchu

Professor of College of Life Science

China West Normal University

October 25, 2014

GIFT FROM
ANCIENT TIMES

FATHER DAVID'S
DISCOVERY

Armand David (September 27, 1826-November 10, 1900) was born in 1826 in Ezpeleta in southwest France, a small city neighboring the Basque region of Spain. That particular era was a time of great discovery in terms of flora and fauna. Not so affected by the Quaternary glaciations of the Ice Age, China had been able to preserve so many remarkable rare animals and plants that "going to China" had become a trend among zoologists and botanists. Influenced by his father, David combined religious piety with a strong interest in nature, reflecting in the collection of insect specimens. A decade after becoming a Lazarist missionary Catholic priest, David was finally dispatched to China. During those 10 years, he studied natural history and the handling of specimens in Florence and could vividly mimic the chirps of various creatures, in preparation for his great Chinese treasure hunt.

In February 1869, David arrived in Dengchigou in the Qionglai Mountain, Muping County (today's Baoxing County of Sichuan Province). It was a transitional zone lying between the lush Sichuan Basin and the arid Qinghai-Tibet Plateau. Numerous mountains stretch from west to east, but are suddenly traversed by a range running north-south. Consequently, a natural T-junction appears to become home to animals and plants moving in from all directions. A Chinese-style two-storied quadrangle dwelling with a huge roof was perched on hilltop at an altitude of 1,765 meters. That was a church founded in 1839.

As soon as David arrived at Dengchigou, he threw himself into collecting specimens of flora and fauna. On one occasion, he lost his way and stumbled upon "the most breathtaking mountain road". On his return after investigating the area around the summit of the Hongshan Mountain, he stopped to rest at the house of a villager named Li. Near the fire pit, a black and

◀ In November 2004, Andre Derraidou, former mayor of Ezpeleta, made a special visit to giant pandas in Dengchigou.

white fur hanging on the wall attracted David's attention. The host explained it was a kind of secretive beast that inhabited the high mountains and dense forests on that area that he and his fellow-villagers called "Hua Xiong" (colorful bear). One of the villagers promised to give David a live cub. Unfortunately, by the time the cub reached David, the animal stopped breathing due to the jolting experienced on the rough road.

According to strict regulations of zoological taxonomy, one cannot identify a species without the actual presence of a fur or even body or skeleton. Finally, on April 1, a hunter caught a live "Hua Xiong" and brought it to David.

This was an adult giant panda, and more exuberant, stronger and attractive than those pudgy pandas seen in the zoo. Under the scouring influence of rain, frost and dew, and being swept by branches and grass leaves, its fur sparkled - the black fur looked like black paint and the white fur looked like silver.

That very night, David hurriedly wrote a report to Henri Milne-Edwards, the eminent zoologist who was curator of the National Museum of Natural History of Paris. He thought this peculiar animal was a kind of bear, and named it Black and White Bear. However, Henri Milne-

Portrait of Armand David.

Portraits of giant panda and Chinese elk collected by Father David.

Edwards did not accept the fact that there was any relationship between the panda and bear. After several twists and turns, it was eventually given the name of "giant panda".

It is believed that there are dozens of names in Chinese classics, such as Mo (Tapir), Hua Xiong, White Leopard, Shitieshou (Iron-eating Beast), Pi Xiu (Mythical Wild Animal), White Fox, which are suspected to have referred to the giant panda at different times. So, why was David given the honor of its discovery?

The word is appropriate in the sense of modern science, because the scientific name was based on the requirements of animal taxonomy and abided by the internationally recognized standard. Since April 1, 1869, Dengchigou, Baoxing County, Sichuan Province has been regarded as the origin of the species.

David's report to the National Museum of Natural History of Paris, and Milne-Edwards' expert 27-page analysis were once published by the museum's journal. The two dust-laden documents stored for 140 years are literally the identification papers of the giant panda, whose full texts have never been read by contemporary scientists before.

In recent years, a panda-lover, Sun Qian, the former deputy mayor of Ya'an City, asked his

The Origin of the Name of 'Giant Panda'

Henri Milne-Edwards studied the fur and skeleton of the panda as well as David's report, and concluded that, although there were some similarities, its teeth and skeletal features were very different. Besides, it had an apomorphic relationship with the raccoon and Chinese Lesser Panda. Considering that the bamboo-eating Lesser Panda was already found in Himalayan foothills in 1825, this new species was named Giant Panda.

Lesser Panda and Giant Panda.

189 species of plants, found by Father David, now engraved in handrails by the Baoxing River.

French friends to look for the two precious documents. After many failures, UNESCO experts - German expert Dr. Gerhard Kutsch and British expert Dr. Wyn Courtney and her husband - found them by using the extraordinarily large data bank of the National Museum of Natural History of Paris in February 2009. They were thrilled and personally delivered the copies of the two documents to China.

Some 140 years ago, it took Armand David six days to travel from Chengdu to Baoxing on foot. Nowadays, it only takes three hours by bus. At nine o'clock on the morning of February 27, 2009, a Ceremony of Donating Precious Type Specimen Document of the Giant Panda by the National Museum of Natural History of Paris was held at the Dengchigou Church. Besides the local government officials, some 100 local villagers attended. Dr. Gerhard Kutsch on behalf of the National Museum of Natural History of Paris gave the two precious documents to Baoxing County.

It would surely surprise Armand David to know that 140 years after his discovery a giant panda fever would sweep the world.

Portrait of Armand David.

In the picture taken in front of a church are Dr. Gerhard Kutsch, a German expert with UNESCO (second right), Dr. Wyn Courtney, a British expert with UNESCO (third right), Professor He Fenqi of the Animal Research Institute of the Chinese Academy of Sciences (first right), French diplomat Emmanuel Pollet (third left), former vice mayor of Ya'an City Sun Qian (second left) and author Tan Kai (left).

WHO WAS THE ANCESTOR
OF THE PANDA

The exhibiting of the giant panda skin at the National Museum of Natural History of Paris aroused a sensation in 1870. Paleontologists began to ask who was the ancestor of the unique animal.

For a long time, the Hungarian "Agriarcros goaci" was academically regarded as the ancestor of the East Asian panda. In other words, the giant pandas widely distributed in East Asia were a "European species of the Chinese origin". On this point, Professor Pei Wenzhong, a world-known prehistoric archaeologist, who was the first discoverer of the skull of Peking Man, had doubts, based on both his abundant knowledge and sharp academic sense.

Professor Pei believed that the alleged linkage with "Agriarcros goaci" was unconvincing due to lack of solid supporting evidence. More importantly, he found Ailuropoda microta, a Ailuropoda microta.

In the early 1950s, the South China cave expedition led by Pei Wenzhong arrived in Guangxi. They unearthed 79 fossils of the small panda species after repeated exploration for seven years in the nitrate cave in Liuzhou.

Pei Wenzhong believed that though the small panda species found in the nitrate cave dated back more than 2 million years, it was clearly distinct from the Ailuropoda melanoleuca baconi that appeared much later, but as surely the ancestor of the living panda.

In the meantime, Pei Wenzhong had talked with Huang Wanbo of the younger generation that the origin of the panda awaited further investigation and research.

In the 1960s, during the construction of the Chengdu-Kunming Railway, a great sensation was caused by the discovery of vertebrate fossils in Shihuiba Village, Lufeng County, Yunnan Province. The identification of several ursidae fossils as "Divisia Ursavus" attracted the interest of Huang Wanbo, who was then studying the origin of the panda. Through the restudy of "Divisia Ursavus", scholars found that between the ursavus and the panda, there was Ailuaractos Lufengensis dating back eight million years and Ailurarctos Yuanmouensis dating back seven million years.

Professor Huang Wanbo spent a lot of energy and finally clarified the evolution of the panda - from omnivore (Ursavus) to omnivore accompanied by occasionally eating some bamboos (Ailurarctos), to bamboo-eating with omnivore episodes occasionally (Ailuropoda microta), to mainly eating bamboos (Ailuropoda melanoleuca baconi) and finally to the living giant panda.

Since 8 million years ago, a number of ancient animals became extinct, but the pandas remained in the bamboo forests in the mountains, even refusing to evolve.

The bones of those animals living on the Earth nowadays including wolves and black bears are relatively "hollow" and lighter; however, the bones of pandas are almost "solid" and hence quite heavy.

▲ Professor Huang Wanbo gathering panda fossils in Lufeng.

▼ Professor Pei Wenzhong (middle) unearthed fossils of the small panda species after repeated explorations in the nitrate cave in Liuzhou, Guangxi Zhuang Autonomous Region.

The Hey Day of the Panda Kingdom

A complete maxilla bone of the panda named Ailuropoda melanoleuca baconi was discovered in the cave in the Ruby Mine in Mogok, Myanmar in 1915. Walter Willis Granger, an American vertebrate paleontologist, later discovered panda fossils from the same historical period in Yanjinggou area, Wanxian County, Sichuan Province. Both belong to a subspecies called "Ailuropoda melanoleuca baconi" in China, whose size was one-third of Ailuropoda microta. This particular animal lived on the East Asian continent about 1 million years ago, when there were pandas in Chinese regions from the Yunnan-Guizhou Plateau in the west to Anhui Province in the east, to Zhoukoudian in the north, and to Hainan Island in the south, in Myanmar and the northern part of Vietnam. This was the peak period of the Panda Kingdom.

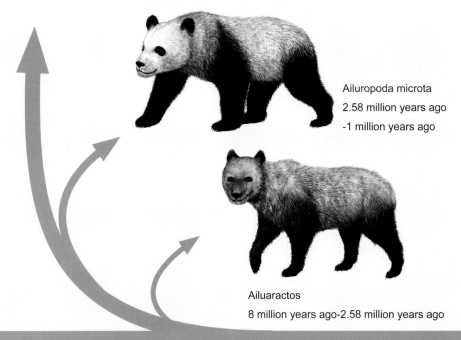

Ailuropoda melanoleuca baconi
1 million years ago-30 thousand years ago

Ailuropoda microta
2.58 million years ago
-1 million years ago

Ailuaractos
8 million years ago-2.58 million years ago

Teeth of Ailuaractos Lufengensis.   Teeth of Ailurarctos.

Maxillary fragments of Ailurarctos Yuanmouensis.

19

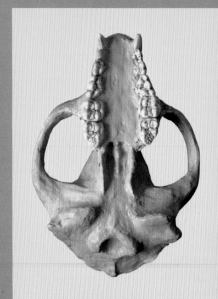

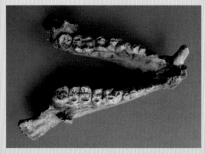

Chewing surface of a small panda skull.

Lower jawbone of the small panda first discovered in China.

How about measuring the panda's brain capacity? It is only 310-320 ml, 60 ml smaller than that of the black bear of similar size.

Now look at the panda's skull, which is almost the same as the skull fossils of 900,000 years ago. As the panda has the characteristics of ancient animals such as heavy skeleton and small brain capacity, it is very appropriate to call it a "living fossil".

In 2001, when a Sino-foreign joint expedition was examining a "Tiankeng"(karst topography) in Leye, Guangxi Zhuang Autonomous Region, they received from a local man some pieces of animal fossils which he had found in a karst cave in Huaping Town. The team of experts rushed to the town immediately.

The cave entrance was so narrow that it was necessary to crawl to gain access. Lights shone on the cave walls revealed variously shaped white inlays, which were fossils. They included seven kinds of rare mammal fossils over 2 million years ago, including panda, deer, tapir, stegodon, rhinoceros and wild boar. The cave was virtually a fossil museum of ancient animals.

The experts affirmed that the fossil they had been given was the most complete giant panda specimen to date. The fossil tells of a stronger function of grinding food and big molars of simpler structure compared with that of the living panda, and is clearly smaller than the living panda, according to which it can be estimated that the panda at that time was in a transition from eating meat to eating bamboos, which shows it should be Ailuropoda microta living about two million years ago.

The complete fossil dating back about 2 million years discovered in Tiankeng, Leye County, is the strongest evidence of "the big diffusion of small species panda" in biological history.

GOD'S CREATION WITH
SIGNIFICANT MEANING

In 1961, zoologists from around the world got together and agreed that the panda patterns designed by Englishman Sir Peter Scott should be the flag and emblem of the World Wildlife Fund (WWF).

A WWF declaration states that "the panda is not only the precious treasure of the Chinese people, but also a valuable heritage of natural history for people all over the world".

Igor Petrovich Sinofsky, famous former Soviet zoologist and director of the Moscow Zoo, spoke highly of the giant pandas: "The giant panda is an original, unique and incredible animal as well as a true treasure on the Earth."

The experts studying animal aesthetics marveled that "the giant panda is a cartoon image delicately designed by God".

Firstly, the likable chubby round face of the giant panda is simple and honest but naughty, which makes it look like chubby child wearing sunglasses. Besides, its two big round ears look like black velvet flowers atop its head. What's more, the feature of short rhynchodaenm of the giant panda conforms to people's aesthetic taste.

Actually, the skull of the giant panda is very similar to that of many mammals. Its round face is caused by the constant eating of bamboo. In the process, the panda's facial muscles become well developed to produce the typical fat cheeks.

In addition, the black and white fur of panda is rare in the animal world. Black and white, warm and cool, are two striking contrasts forming a gorgeous but elegant, noble but refined visual effect. Moreover, black and white are two quite highlighted colors against the background of the green forest make other animals dodge pandas so that conflicts are avoided. The black and white of pandas are really the colors of wisdom.

Some experts think that it is very important for pandas to protect their eyes, noses, and limbs to live in the cold immense forest on the high mountains. Black can absorb heat. After a long period of life experience and adaptation, pandas have developed black eye rims, black ears, black nose and black arms and legs.

When observing the panda walking, you will find that their bottoms are swinging - just like fashion models on the T-shaped catwalk. If you observe more carefully, you will notice that both the foreleg and hind legs of the panda lean to the inside, and form a typical "pigeon toe" effect, differing from the black bear whose hind legs alone lean to the inside.

Later, you will hear that pandas are born to be carnivorous animals. Once they begin to eat meat, they can never stop. However, pandas impress people as firm vegetarians after seeing them consume bamboo for a long time.

About 2 to 3 million years ago, China was in the the Quaternary Glacier Period. The weather was very cold and the Earth was like a gigantic shroud. Even the most aggressive predators, the saber-toothed tigers that were on the top of the food chain, became extinct.

Not All Pandas are Black and White

In March 1985, Dandan, a brown and white panda, was first found in the Foping Nature Reserve in the Qinling Mountains (a major east-west mountain range in southern Shaanxi Province). More of this type were found thereafter. In November 2009, scientists found a panda baby that had been abandoned by its mother. The panda baby Qi Zai was the seventh brown and white panda found in the Qinling Mountains. Scientists have conducted studies on this, but without results so far.

Giant panda paintings by Tan Kai, author of the book.

Pandas, as neighbors of the saber-toothed tigers, fed on bamboos, and survived stubbornly, showing their natural instincts of avoiding dangers. The true experiences of the pandas demonstrates the "survival of the fittest" theory put forward by Charles Robert Darwin (1809-1882).

It may be assumed that pandas unintentionally practice the "philosophy" of Lao Tse (an influential Chinese philosopher and the founder of Taoism) and Chuang Tzu (an influential Chinese philosopher). The core of their philosophy is "letting nature take its course" and "the highest good is like that of water".

A poem once describes that the giant panda is the moving diagram of the universe, and the diagram of the universe is the still giant panda. The philosophy of this poem is too wonderful for words. God's creation is full of profound implications.

VIDEO

Why Black and White

THE 51G PANDA THAT
MOVED THE JAPANESE

Why are Panda Babies so Small?

The newly born panda babies look exactly like flesh pink rats. Their weight can only be the 1,000th that of their mum. Actually, the whole process of natural mating, getting pregnant and delivery can range from 76 to 180 days. Why are the panda babies so small? It is caused by typical "delayed implantation".

In fact, when the female pandas mate successfully, the seed of life should appear in the uterus wall, just like seeds in the earth. Then, the germ cell can obtain nutrition from the matrix, and grow day by day as normal. However, just as the panda always wanders in the forest, the "seed" also likes to wander in the womb. It will only become implanted 34 days before delivery, which explains why the panda baby is so small. All the panda babies are, thus, "premature infants".

In April 1963, the pandas Pi Pi and Li Li from the Beijing Zoo succeeded in natural mating.

From then on, two female experts Ouyang Gan and Huang Huilan conducted specific management and a monographic study on Li Li. In the early September, it suffered loss of appetite, with abnormal behavior; however, despite all their care, experts missed the opportunity of observing parturition. On September 9, to their surprise, they found that a pink small "meatball" appeared in Li Li's arms, which was quite beyond their expectations. They once estimated that the panda baby should have weight several kilograms. However, what they saw was a tiny baby as small as a newborn rat, half transparent, and weighing less than 100 grams. At first, the experts thought it conjectured that there had been a miscarriage, which really depressed them. Fortunately, they found the panda baby emitted loud sounds and its vital signs were normal. Then, they wept for joy.

For the first time, people got to know that the panda baby could be so small.

Professor Pan Wenshi from Peking University thinks that the giant pandas choose to deliver a small baby instead of a big one for the purpose of adapting well to their living environment. The germ cell cannot absorb a bigger molecular-weight of fatty

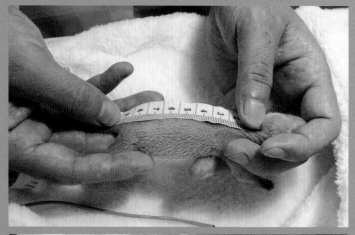

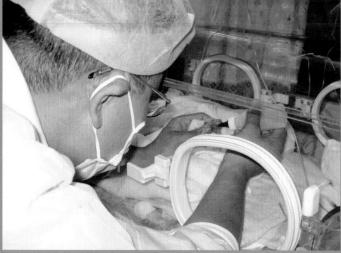

Newborn 51g panda.

VIDEO

Newborn panda
baby

acid from the matrix, so it can only wait for the hydrolyzed protein from there to change into a smaller molecular-weight glucose, and provide nutrition. If the pregnancy is too long, excessive consumption of the protein will threaten the panda mother's life. Hence, both mother and child will only be safe if the panda baby is delivered early, and lives on its mother's milk. When the fat decomposes into fatty acid, milk will be formed and flow easily.

Around early autumn, when the pregnant panda mothers are going to give birth in the mountains, they will choose a tree hole or a rock nest that is shady and quiet, but near to bamboos or water, and prepare some leaves and branches; they will also plane some sawdust from the tree holes to create a soft obstetric table ready for delivery.

Those panda mothers in a captive environment do not need to find themselves a place for delivery, for this will already have been prepared by the working staff who maintain 24-hour monitoring of the each and every move. All are waiting for the solemn moment when a new life emerges.

On August 7, 2006, Qi Zhen, a giant panda in the Chengdu Research Base of Giant Panda Breeding, gave birth to twins. Another little panda slipped out of the birth canal and fell onto the ground after the older twin was born. It struggled on the ice-cold ground and remained still after rolling a few times. The researchers put it into the incubator right away. It was the rarely seen super small panda baby, with the weight of 51 grams (the name 51g then given to it).

Normally, the weight of the newly born panda babies is around 150 grams, so this one was only a third of normal! It didn't have gyrus (ridge on the cerebral cortex) and sulcus (groove on the brain surface). There were no white blood cells. Its renal function was not fully

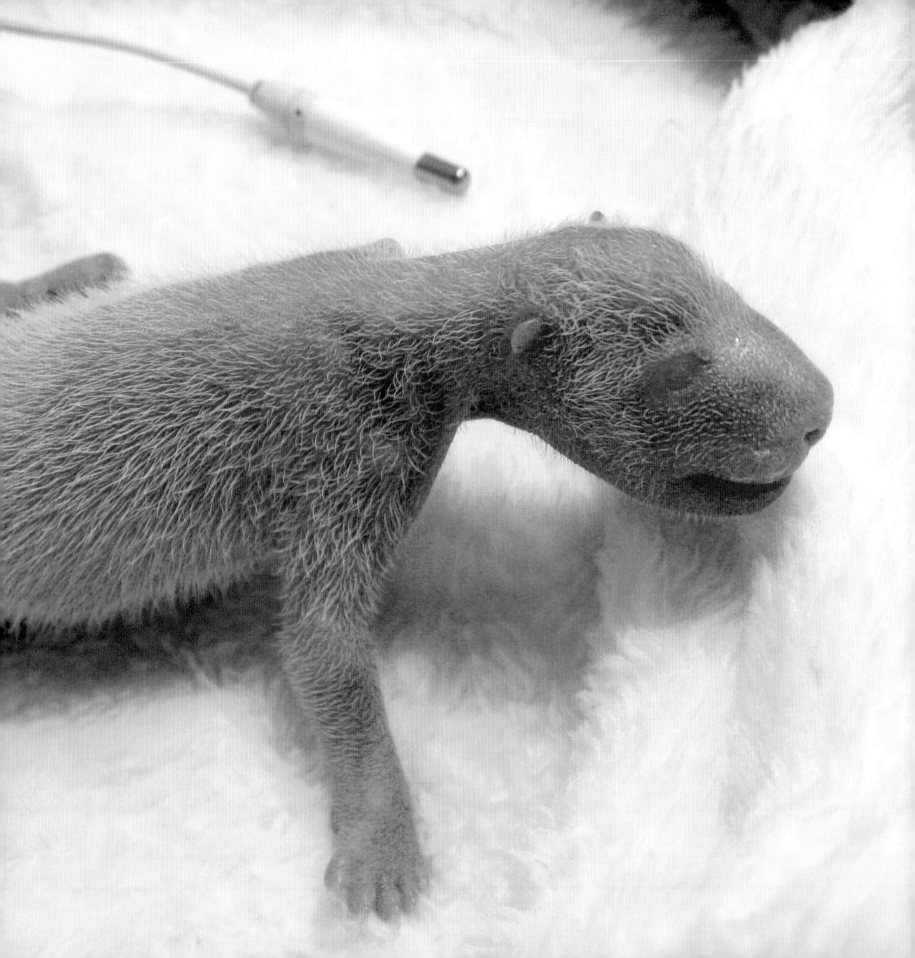

developed. Its body temperature was only 34 degrees. All these indicated that 51g was so weak it might die at any moment.

It had been warmed up in the arms of one of the staff for three hours before its temperature returned to normal. However, staff noticed its mouth was even smaller than the papilla of Qi Zhen, its mum, which meant breast-feeding was impossible. As we all know, panda babies not fed on milk can never survive. So, staff took the risk and got the milk from Qi Zhen. 51g couldn't even take the initiative to swallow when it was first fed and staff had to squeeze the milk into its mouth and let it gradually flow into its throat. It took as long as half an hour to deliver 0.8 ml of milk at first. Huang Xiangming, one of the carers, was sweating all over after feeding 51g. He was afraid that 51g would choke on the milk and suffocate due to his carelessness.

51g grew stronger and stronger because of the milk drops. Everyone closely monitored the little poor thing, and would feed 51g before its twin brother. The appetite of 51g was rather good and it grew really fast. After three years, 51g grew up to weigh 105 kg, which was 2,000 times compared with the weight when it's born!

51g panda and its brother.

51g panda enjoys good health.

Qi Zhen, the mother of 51g, also created a life miracle. Mei Mei, the grandmother of 51g, was scared by the loud cries of its daughter when it gave birth to Qi Zhen, its first pregnancy. It threw the baby on its back in panic and intended to climb up the steel bars and escape. In the process, Qi Zhen's chest was lacerated and blood began to ooze out of the wound. The researchers saved Qi Zhen's life by inserting seven stitches in the wound. It was then named Qi Zhen (with a similar pronunciation in Chinese to "seven stitches") in memory of the accident.

Later, Mei Mei became a competent panda mother as well as a world-renowned heroine. During its long stay in Japan, it gave birth to nine panda babies through five pregnancies; seven babies survived. According to common practice, panda mothers can only feed one baby and would tend to abandon the relatively weaker one in the case of

Weighing the 51g panda.

51g panda in mother's arm.

twins. However, Mei Mei hated to part with either of the twins. It held them tightly in its arms and fed them one by one so that both grew up well. Mei Mei set a world record in feeding two panda babies at the same time without the help of workers.

When 51g was born in Chengdu, it didn't arouse much attention of the Chinese media, but it did attract Zhang Yunhui, a Chinese film producer who resides in Japan. Soon after the birth of 51g, the camera crew traveled from Japan to follow and recorded the growth process of 51g, and accumulated rich materials.

On March 11, 2011, an earthquake of 9 magnitude occurred in the Tokai area of Japan. Over 10,000 people died and thousands of others were missing. The worrying images and enormous losses made every person with a conscience reflect on the tragedies that can occur to every human being.

On February 6, 2012, *Story of Giant Panda 51g* was released in the disaster area of Japan. For those Japanese people who just suffered disaster, the film was cozy, comfortable, inspirational and edificatory and demonstrated that hope can only be acquired if you never let go, if you stand firmly and indomitably, and if you believe failure is not even an option when you are faced with unfortunate and hopeless situations. Thus 51g reached into the hearts of the Japanese people.

◀ "Daddy" Huang Xiangming and his giant pandas.

▶ Big-boy 51g giant panda.

PANDA MOTHERS WITH
DIFFERENT PERSONALITIES

Experts started to gain a preliminary understanding of panda motherhood after Li Li gave birth in the Beijing Zoo in 1963. Unlike black bears, panda mothers don't react violently towards strangers. Later, more and more captive-bred pandas give birth and some of the young mothers got panicked by the cries of their babies and even tried to flee. Some weren't able to hold their babies and couldn't act like competent mothers in terms of nursing. There was wide divergence in such behavior.

However, what about panda mothers living in the wild?

In March 1981, a female panda named Zhen Zhen was caught near the field observation station in Wolong Town, Wenchuan County of Ya'an City in Sichuan Province. The staff put a wireless neck strap around the panda's neck while it was sedated and then released its back into the wild. Afterwards, a study of the signals emitted by the device helped domestic and foreign experts to understand the panda daily routine amid the bamboo groves.

They deliberately sought to avoid meeting Zhen Zhen directly, although they did once cross its path. Judging from changes of Zhen Zhen's feeding habits, the experts concluded it must be pregnant and later had given birth as the signal indicated it stayed in the same location.

◀ Mother holds its newborn baby in the mouth in the first few months.

Dr. George Beals Schaller, a world famous zoologist, together with Professor Hu Jinchu, a Chinese panda research expert, decided to visit Zhen Zhen based on its radio location about a month after it was assumed to have given birth. The two experts sought to proceed carefully along the path covered by leaves in the shaded bamboo groves.

As they got closer, they could even hear the loud cries of the panda baby. These were out of all proportion to its diminutive size, which may be a self-defense device to frighten away its natural enemies.

Zhen Zhen suddenly rushed out at these two unexpected guests with thunderous roars right after Hu Jinchu raised his camera, and the two experts had no choice but to flee. Hu Jinchu noticed that Schaller was climbing up a tree and was afraid that Zhen Zhen would hurt him as pandas are excellent tree climbers. So, he led Zhen Zhen in another direction on purpose, and a thrilling chase thus began.

Hu Jinchu was quite familiar with the surrounding terrain, and knew pandas are slow in climbing mountains and clumsy when turning around. So he chose a zigzagging uphill path. After ten minutes, Zhen Zhen was out of breath. Standing only a few meters from each other,

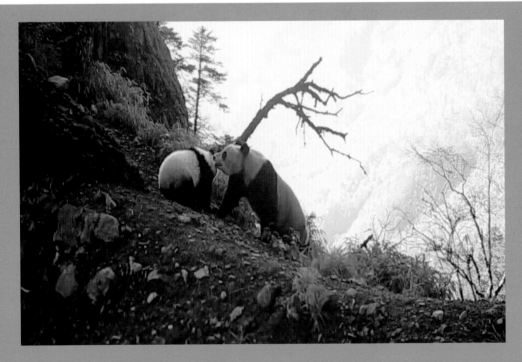

Sichuan Anzihe Nature Reserve: Two wild pandas, one big and one small, passed through infrared camera on October 21, 2013. As the panda baby tried to linger before the camera lens, its mother gave it a "push" with its mouth to hide in the bamboo groves.

to feed, it would leave Huzi in the cave, and Professor Pan and her students, as well as Xiang Bangfa. would take the chance and collect information about the baby's health condition. One time, when Jiao Jiao arrived back at the cave entrance, it saw Professor Pan was still playing with Huzi. it didn't roar or shout, and just sat quietly aside, as if saying, "as long as Huzi doesn't create a disturbance, help yourself". Professor Pan hurriedly returned Huzi to Jiao Jiao who immediately began to nurse it.

Huzi was thus on intimate terms with humans from birth. Jiao Jiao and Huzi, in fact, were rare pandas maintaining a close relationship with humans. Sometimes, when you greeted them, they would come and play, or hum in response if busy eating bamboos.

Jiao Jiao later gave birth to Xi Wang and Xiao San. According to the number of Jiao Jiao's family members, the year-on-year growth rate of wild pandas is 4 percent, which is not low. The research carried out on Jiao Jiao's family by Professor Pan helped expand people's vision and has been of significant scientific value. The book *Giant Panda Huzi*, compiled on the basis of his 12 years of experiences, has become a classic science book enjoying great popularity at home and abroad.

Hu Jinchu and Zhen Zhen could even hear each other's wheezing. They stared at each other, but neither of them had the strength to walk another step. Finally, Hu Jinchu climbed up a cliff face, and Zhen Zhen left in a huff.

In the comic situation like the movie *Guardie e ladri* (an Italian movie released in the early 1950s), Zhen Zhen, unlike the docile and tolerant panda seen in ordinary times, demonstrated strong maternal instincts in order to protect its baby. In contrast, Jiao Jiao, another panda mother living in the Qinling Mountains of Shaanxi Province, was quite generous.

In the early spring of 1985, Professor Pan Wenshi from Peking University came across Jiao Jiao in the Shaanxi Changqing Nature Reserve. With the help of a forest zone worker named Xiang Bangfa, Jiao Jiao was sedated and fitted with a wireless neck strap top become a research panda providing plenty of information.

After a year, Jiao Jiao grew even prettier. it fell in love with a handsome male panda in early spring and gave birth to a panda baby in August. According to the observation records, Jiao Jiao didn't feed over a period of 40 days for the sake of its beloved baby. It let the baby sleep in its arms and never touched the ground during that time.

Professor Pan and his colleagues found Jiao Jiao and its baby in an extremely dangerous cave. it was holding the baby and showed no surprise for their coming maybe because it was very familiar with the odors of Professor Pan and Xiang Bangfa. People described Jiao Jiao as a "generous farm-wife from the north". Professor Pan Wenshi named the panda baby Huzi. Afterwards, when Jiao Jiao went out

MICHELLE OBAMA FEEDS
APPLES TO PANDAS

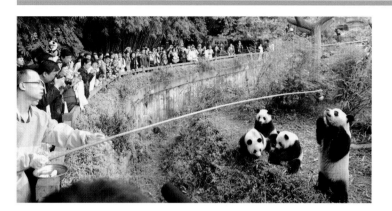

At around 10 o'clock on March 26, 2014, Michelle Obama, the wife of US President Obama, came to visit the Chengdu Research Base of Giant Panda Breeding together with her mother and daughters. They walked through the Bamboo Corridor and stepped onto a tree-shaded green grassland where the 22-year-old panda mother Li Li, and five-year-old panda babies attracted their attention. "Wow, they are so cute!"

Those youngsters looked just like big fluffy dolls and were the age of artlessness and cheerfulness. Some of them hung from branches while others climbed up and down the trees. Their chubby bodies twisted every now and then, greatly amusing the Obama party.

They were then invited to feed apples to the pandas.

Bamboo poles with apples on one end were stretched through the handrails and across the moats one after one. The pandas, having smelt the scent of apples, stood up, opened their mouths and tried to bite them.

Why should people feed apples like this? Is there any meaning for pandas to stand up and bite apples? We need to start from an understanding of the breeding situation of captive-bred pandas.

In September 1963, Li Li gave birth to Ming Ming in the Beijing Zoo, which was the first breeding record captive-bred environment. However, the remaining pandas didn't get pregnant despite repeated efforts by the zoo over many years.

Ling Ling, another giant panda, had given birth to four babies from 1972 when it settled in the National Zoological Park in Washington DC to 1999 when it died of illness, but none survived.

Experts exclaimed that there are three difficulties facing the breeding of captive giant pandas - oestrus, hybridization and fertilization, as well as survival.

Let's first look over the oestrus difficulty.

In order to bring pandas on heat, experts had tried many methods, but none were effective. Some people even joked that those methods had even brought the breeders on heat, but not the pandas.

After repeated research, the experts realized where the problem lay and put forward effective counter-measures.

First, compared with the enriched surroundings in the wild, the animal houses seemed like jails with the activity space rather limited. With the passage of time, the pandas grew more rigid and lost interest in love and romance.

This led to creation of applied environmental enrichment technology. The experts created a diversified living environment and expanded the living space for pandas. Thus, the energy and activity levels of the pandas were significantly enhanced.

Second, pandas can choose different foods in the wild, and different bamboos can provide balanced nutrition. However, in

▲ Video shows two pandas mating to lure others to mate.

▼ Male and female pandas in separate cages: they see all day long so as to develop desire for mating.

◀ Success in natural mating.

▶ Two pandas mated naturally in the San Diego Zoo on April 9, 2005.

48

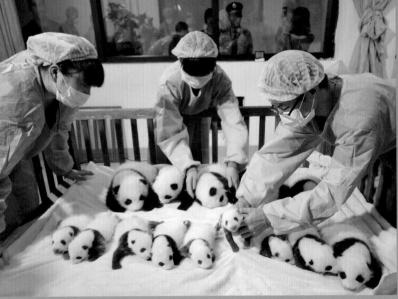

▲ Artificial fertilization of a giant panda.

▼ Fourteen panda babies born in 2013 in the Chengdu Research Base of Giant Panda Breeding.

captivity, pandas have no choice but to eat unitary bamboos, leading to declining health and influencing the oestrus conditions.

In response, the experts choose to add artificial mixed feed as well as fruit and vegetables through the modification of the panda's food structure and feeding modes. They intensified the replenishment amount of nutritional ingredients like micro-elements and protein to form a well-balanced food structure. They also advocate several small meals for the pandas and increased activity levels, which has helped to improve panda physique.

Additionally, the experts help to induce oestrus of female and male pandas during the fertile period such as exchanging the female and male housing regularly to stimulate the pandas and raise their desire to mate.

Such measures have ensured 90 percent of female pandas of childbearing age will have normal oestrus.

Now, let's move on to the difficulty of hybridization and fertilization.

The experts have been thinking about improving the pregnancy rate of female captive-bred pandas through artificial insemination on the basis of natural mating or through complete artificial insemination.

As early as the 1980s, the Chengdu Zoo was probing into the key technologies to acquire, dilute, freeze and unfreeze semen. The China Research and Conservation Center for the Giant Panda (CRCCGP), located in Wolong Town, has also been carrying out similar research. In 1996, a breeding expert from the National Zoological Park in Washington DC, came to China and showed local staff that the formula to dilute the semen was the key to sperm vitality. A best formula was selected after years of tackling key problems and sifting through several dozen formulae.

The ovulation cycle of giant pandas can be grasped accurately through various technologies monitoring the hormone levels of female pandas. Choosing the proper time, carrying out natural mating and assisting with artificial insemination proved a fail-safe method. The fresh and alive sperms hit the ovum like unmistakable bullets and create fertilized ovum.

So why make pandas stand up and eat apples? The goal is to work on the hind limb strength of male pandas to perform well in natural mating.

With the problem of hybridization and fertilization tackled, that left only one difficulty.

FOSTER PANDA BABIES
- THE HARDEST TIME

The hardships panda mothers suffer are rarely seen among mammals!

Panda mothers would hug their offspring in the first few days after birth. Once the panda babies begin to cry, the mothers would instantly change a posture to ensure the babies could sleep more comfortably. This is because panda mothers are a thousand times heavier than their offspring and would hurt them if not very careful.

After parturition, the mothers would keep licking their own fetal blood (lochia) and the babies' excrement, which is a habit generated from the cruel wild living conditions. That's because the odor of fetal blood and excrement is quite strong and easy to spread, which would attract predators.

Panda mothers living in the wild have to face starvation and feed panda babies with valuable milk in different weather conditions outside the tree holes or caves or in the pitch-black forests. The skin of panda babies doesn't have the ability to stay warm or cool down, so panda mothers have to keep licking the babies and let them sleep on their chests to help maintain a normal body temperature. They place the babies in the maternity spots, cover them with leaves and only then go off to feed or drink water. Even then, they remain on high alert for any sign of disturbance or trouble with their ears while paying attention to the foreign smells of the cunning and cruel natural enemies like martes flavigula, golden cats and cuon alpinus, which may sneak into the tree holes and attack panda babies. Strict precautions are needed.

Many unexpected dangers are hidden in the seemingly tranquil forest.

In the China Research and Conservation Center for the Giant Panda of Wolong and the Chengdu Research Base of Giant Panda Breeding, people there have grown familiar with the eyes of panda mothers in confinement.

They are terribly fatigued eyes that may close at any time but still struggle to stay open. They are really melancholy eyes.

An average of 48 percent of panda mothers may give birth to twin babies, but due to the unfavorable living environment they may choose to abandon one in order to improve the survival chances of the other. Besides, some panda mothers lack experience and are not competent enough to raise little pandas. Therefore, the survival rate of artificial reproduction is only 33 percent. The key to increasing the survival rate and to raise twin panda babies is to let experienced panda mothers feed the babies that are short of milk.

If the abandoned panda babies are fed artificially, two more difficulties emerge: First, what temperature should the incubator be kept at? Second, what kind of milk should be used?

In the beginning, the Chengdu Zoo followed the experience in feeding tiger or lion cubs. The staff would make a wooden box with a bulb inside to maintain a temperature of around 30 degrees; however, it turned out that the panda babies died of cold within two or three days.

Mother and son in the wild.

So what is the proper temperature for the incubator? It is really troublesome!

In 1988, Mei Mei, a panda from Chengdu, gave birth to twins. Staff took turns to wrap the baby in little towels and hug it tight to pass on their own warmth.

The baby slept in the arms of its nannies quietly and grew bigger and bigger by the day. Afterwards, veterinarians managed to get the temperature of the heat generated by panda mother's arms - between 36 and 37 degrees Centigrade. Later, automatic incubators appeared where the temperature could be carefully regulated.

It was even more troublesome to determine what kind of milk powder should be used. Experts had tried cow's milk powder, ewe's milk powder and imported milk powder, and finally decided to try human breastfeeding.

Staff were sent to seek human milk from local hospital delivery rooms. A female worker named Chen who had just given birth had plenty of milk to offer. it installed a bed near the panda delivery room and volunteered to sacrifice its milk to feed the panda babies.

For the future of panda families, an ordinary female worker generously sacrificed the milk that should have been given to its own child, which truly moved many experts to tears.

Twin pandas

VIDEO

However, it was a pity that the panda baby still didn't survive with human milk.

Huan Huan, a panda mother in Japan, gave birth to Tong Tong. Japanese scientists collected a drop of colostrum (first milk) that fell to the ground for analysis and duplication. But no matter how they tried, the synthesized milk couldn't replace the colostrum that panda mothers secrete. It looks like watery green juice, but it contains rich antibodies that humans couldn't produce. Only panda babies fed on original colostrum could have a chance to survive.

All this meant that, if a panda mother gives birth to twin babies, A and B, staff would have to take away B and let the mother feed A first. Then, the staff would find a way to replace A with B, so the twins could take turns to feed on the colostrum.

But this was a very risky strategy! At the Chengdu Research Base of Giant Panda Breeding in 1989, the breeders and veterinarians once tried to place a panda baby coated with the urine of Mei Mei into the latter's arms; however, Mei Mei got angry and stepped on one panda baby and bit the other, so that both died.

In 1990, Qing Qing gave birth to another pair of twins that delighted the staff even though it also brought difficulties. Considering the failure with Mei Mei, should they try again? After much discussion

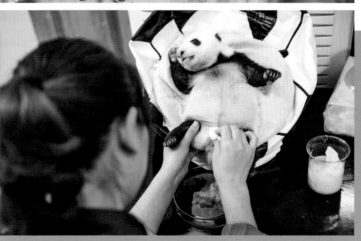

Better care for newborn panda babies.

and research it was decided to try again. They could never progress if they didn't take any risks.

One of the breeders placed a pot of milk in front of Qing Qing to block its view; then, one of the newly born babies was spirited away while Qing Qing focused on the milk pot; it didn't notice what was happening.

When the newly born baby in Qing Qing's arms was full, the breeder tried to replace it with the second one. Maybe the breeder got too nervous, or maybe Qing Qing noticed. The breeder didn't dare to walk too close to Qing Qing, so he put the panda baby coated with the mother's urine on the ground.

The panda baby looked just like a little mouse without fur, chirping and squirming on the ground to attract Qing Qing's attention. Qing Qing was confused and didn't understand how the baby in its arms had suddenly crawled onto the ground. Qing Qing walked towards the baby, sniffed it, licked it with its pink tongue, and then gently lifted it with its mouth.

They had made it! The two newborn babies both fed on the colostrum. They were exchanged repeatedly and took turns to feed on Qing Qing's milk and artificial composed milk until they both grew rather strong.

Nowadays, the feeding of twin pandas is no longer a problem. The heroine Qing Qing was not only able to raise its own twins, but also helped to feed the babies born of its sisters. It can be the nanny for three or four pandas newborn at the same time. Ya Ya, another competent panda mum, meanwhile, helped to feed the babies of Shu Lan, Qi Yuan and Jiao Zi, who were not competent mothers in this regard.

One week

Birthday

Two weeks

30th day

100th day

60th day

Four months

Half year old

One year old

61

MUM CAN BE A
DEMON COACH

People had already stopped letting off fireworks in Chinese New Year outside the mountains. However, large snowflakes, like velvet flowers, were still flying in the sky in Foping of the Qinling Mountains, making a thick silver cover for the mountains in one night. The panda mother took its 18-month-old baby to seek food in the bamboo groves bending like bows because of the heavy snow. The panda baby had learned all much skill from its mother. While not straying far from her, the baby rolled some bamboo leaves and started to eagerly enjoy a meal. Then it tried to snuggle up to its but got a slap for its trouble. What did that mean? Perhaps, the slap signified that the mum expected the baby to be independent. According to the laws of nature, a baby at the age of 18 months should be about to earn its own living completely. How could the baby grow up if it clung to its mother!

Having enjoyed a meal in this bamboo forest, they started to explore another spot. The panda mum in front took a few steps and turned around only to find the baby was no longer there. it called a few times to the baby, who was trying to follow its mother's footsteps, but was struggling, half submerged in the deep snow. During the first months of life when the baby was not able to walk, the mother moved around by holding the infant in its mouth. This is an inherent skill of the species requiring great skill – if the grip was too light, the baby might fall; if too tight, the baby might get injured.

As the baby had grown to be a plump panda weighing 30-40 kg, the mother was not able to hold it any more; certainly, it could not have moved as trekking in the snow was quite energy-consuming.

Anyway, the baby tacitly understood the situation and climbed up to its mother, who trod into the deep snow and determinedly traveled through the forest.

In February 2011, Xiong Baiquan, the head of the Xihe Protection Station of the Foping Nature Reserve Administration, Shaanxi Province, took a photo of a panda mother carrying its baby while walking in the snow.

The photo is the witness of panda maternal love.

The benevolent panda mother also acts as a trainer, turning somewhat ruthless when teaching the baby to climb trees, to wade through snow, to seek for food and to avoid natural enemies.

After Cao Cao gave birth to its baby Tao Tao, it first taught the cub to climb trees. Zhang Hemin, the director of CRCCGP, described how Tao Tao had already learned how to walk when it was only three months old.

When Tao Tao was four months old, under the training of Cao Cao, it started to learn how to climb trees earlier than other captive-bred pandas. Tao Tao quickly mastered various skills as soon as they were taught. Obviously, panda mothers are great teachers for other captive-bred pandas at the same age of Tao Tao were not able to catch up.

This is an extremely rarely-seen photo. Panda cubs become estranged after a year-and-a-half, with the mother neither friendly nor aloof. Finally, with the mother completely lost interest, the mother panda will participate in the next round of marriage. Here are a pair of giant pandas in Foping, this mother struggling through the deep snow carrying her baby.

When Tao Tao climbed a tree for the first time, it climbed more than a meter while being held in mouth by Cao Cao, who obviously worried the cub might get hurt if it climbed too high and fell down. Gradually, Tao Tao became more and more skillful at climbing. When it reached three or four meters, its mother bellowed and climbed up to fetch it down once again. Mum quickly but gently got held the back of Tao Tao's neck in its mouth.

Tao Tao was certainly fond of climbing trees. Sometimes, it would climb so high that mother couldn't use the usual technique. Then, it would hurriedly climb up an adjacent tree and call in a voice very gentle, a bit like the bleat of a sheep. Hearing the call, Tao Tao would obediently get down from the tree.

When seven-month-old Tao Tao could climb a 10-meter-high tree within no more than 20 seconds!

At the Chengdu Research Base of Giant Panda Breeding, it can be seen frequently that a panda mother, seeming to be fierce and brutal, roars or even bites gently if the baby behaves against its will. it demands the baby to learn exactly according to what it teaches.

It is very beneficial to grasp the tree-climbing skill. When all is well, pandas can have a sleep or simply enjoy the sunshine while lying on a branch; when threatened by a predator, pandas can avoid the danger by climbing high up into a tree.

An old staff member in Wolong once personally witnessed a panda mother teaching its baby to wade into the water:

A panda mother and baby were drinking along a river bank. All of a sudden, there was a sign of disturbance or trouble. The mother jogged along the river bank, chose a shallow place and abruptly threw herself into the water. The baby followed, but began swallowing water, panicked and pulled back. The mother immediately caught the baby in

Mother Cao Cao teaching Tao Tao how to climb the tree.

its mouth, ran a few steps and threw the baby into water violently. The baby had to move up and down and wade across the river following its mother.

Bamboo shoots are the best choice for pandas. From March in the early spring to June in the early summer is the season of "chasing bamboo shoots". During these three months, pandas need to travel hundreds of meters, from the mingled forest at the lower altitude where plenty of bamboo shoots come out at first, up to the fir forest at higher altitude where abundant bamboo sprouts eventually emerge. They can eat about 50 kg of bamboo shoots a day.

The process is as follows: sever a piece of bamboo shoot, bite off the top so that a layer of shell wrapping actual shoots falls off, holding the shoots horizontally to take a few succulent bites. The process is like sharpening a pencil with a knife.

Watching its mother, the baby learns another essential skill.

When the baby is about 18 months to two years old, panda mother would lead it to a place far from their home and abandon it for good. In order to breed again, panda mothers participate in a new round of "choosing a husband". Many male pandas with sexual maturity can't help singing love songs to win the affection of a young female panda.

The newly-abandoned panda baby wanders around to look for its mother. It seeks food when hungry, water when thirsty; escapes to the trees when faced with dangers; sleeps on the branches when tired.

In its dreams, the baby would call its mum, yearning eagerly for mother's warmth its mum's temperature and mum's milk. The baby wakes up only to find the deep forest, flying clouds overhead, sunrise and sunset, and the endless twitter of birds in the secluded valley.

Many years later, mother and child may come across each other again, but without recognition. The mother may look at its child whom it once loved extremely and then walk away silently.

That is the maternal love of a panda.

Will panda cubs play together in the wild?

In captivity, many pandas are born each year. These panda cubs live together and learn to play together, just behave like children in kindergartens. However, in the wild, as pandas love to stay alone, panda cubs do not have chances to meet and play together.

Mother Li Li

VIDEO

A CARNIVOROUS HERMIT
IN THE BAMBOO FOREST

Amid the fresh air of the forest there comes a smell of roasted sheep bones spreading far and far wide. Thoroughly seduced, the panda with mouth greedily drooling heads for the long-awaited delicacies.

There are 15 pandas in the two reserves in Tangjiahe and Wolong, Sichuan Province, that have been lured to settle by the odor of roast sheep bones, pig bones or pork, and then became research pandas adorned with wireless neck straps.

Originally, pandas were carnivores. They were omnivorous and sought to eat meat frequently in the period of small panda species about two million years ago.

It stands to reason that giant pandas should be classified as "herbivores" due to their diet mainly of bamboos. However, they should be classified as authentic carnivores from the perspective of the anatomy of their digestive tracts, physiological characteristics and species evolution. In the scientific classification, giant pandas belong in the Mammalia and Carnivora categories. Unexpectedly, they turn out to belong to the same large family as fierce beasts such as tigers, leopards and wolves. The ancestors of giant pandas were worthy of the name of carnivores based on their features including sharp, strong canine teeth, relatively shorter intestinal canals, and the digestive physiological characteristics of carnivores. Giant pandas inherited those features during the evolution. It was only because of the big changes in the living environment that they adapted their feeding habits and behavior and gradually sought seclusion in mountain bamboo groves for survival.

How could the stout giant pandas survive the change? Almost all the bamboos primarily are made up of cellulose and xylogen both severely short in nutritional content. Due to retaining

Burning sheep bones to lure the giant panda.

Pandas' Food

The principal food of wild giant pandas is bamboo. They eat over 20 kinds of bamboo plants growing in different mountainous areas. The giant pandas choose and feed on different species of bamboos or different parts of the same type. For example, they like to eat bamboo shoots of different types mostly in spring and summer; they mainly feed on bamboo leaves in autumn and bamboo culm (the woody, hollow serial stems) in winter.

the "digestive machinery" of carnivores, it is very difficult for giant pandas to digest bamboos. Therefore, they have to eat a great deal and excrete as soon as possible to meet bodily demands.

Thus, "eating" becomes the main activity in panda life. Adults keep eating while walking, sitting and lying within the range of their dens. When they are tired, they go to sleep for a while. There are no fixed places for eating and sleeping.

No any other animal spends such an inordinate amount of time seeking food regardless of the weather throughout the four seasons!

Apart from eating enough fresh bamboos one day, captive-bred giant pandas are supplied with a kind of "coarse bread" made up of corn, soy and wheat flour and some trace elements. The giant pandas living in foreign zoos, like eating a kind of high-fiber, crispy and sweet biscuit developed by American experts.

In addition, pandas are also fond of honey, apples, sugar cane, carrots, and so on. Apples are a must-have prize for the pandas trained to perform various actions.

An adult panda can eat 10 kg of bamboo leaves, 15 kg of tender bamboo poles and 40 kg of tender bamboo shoots a day. There is no need to worry that pandas bursting from over-eating as the food stays in the stomach for a very short time. Though they eat much, they may excrete up to 100 piles of dung in one day!

The panda's digestive tract has a number of single-cell and multi-cell mucus glands. The glandular secretions can protect the gastrointestinal mucosa from injury and play a role

Panda excrement.

of "lubricant" to help the rough bamboo culms leaves and shoots to pass through the digestive tract. What's more, they can consolidate loose bamboo residue into one piece with a layer of mucus on the surface to facilitate defecation. Thanks to the layer of mucus through which panda leave their DNA, and it is the study of this that helps determine the number of pandas in an area.

Pandas tend to bite bamboos rather than incise them. On the molar chewing surface, there remains some uneven profile of cuspis dentis possessed by their ancestors, and which has a certain function of chewing meat.

Besides the teeth for eating bamboos, there are well-developed chewing muscles on both sides of the cheeks. Thus, the sharp teeth coupled with strong chewing muscles make up any deficiencies in terms of intestines and stomach.

Actually, in 1869, Milne-Edwards from the National Museum of Natural History in Paris found pandas have "six digits", an important feature different from that of ursidae.

Originally, since pandas' ancestors had to change from ferocious carnivores to eating bamboos, many attributes in their physical features also changed. For example, a piece of small wrist bone (radial sesamoid) on the forelimb shifted forward and became a new "thumb". The original thumb became parallel with the other four digits. From a functional perspective, the forefoot has six digits, entirely to facilitate feeding on bamboos.

After pandas gradually adapt to eating bamboo plants, they secluded themselves in the bamboo forests to enjoy a leisurely and happy life as true hermits. Due to the abundance of bamboo plant resources, there aren't many animals actually fighting with pandas for food except when red pandas turn up and when the animals like the red deer ruin bamboos while feeding on them. Thus, according the law of nature "use it or lose it", the aggressiveness of pandas degenerated correspondingly. Their limbs became short and thick, making pandas weak in running after small prey. The long-term seclusion in groves with dark light gradually weakened their sights and self-defense capability so that they can only resist natural enemies with their acute sense of smell and by climbing trees.

Though pandas are accustomed to eating vegetation, it doesn't mean that they don't like meat. Given an opportunity, they will expose the true features of carnivores.

On January 4, 1984, a panda named Bei Bei by the faculty paid a visit to the field observation station of Wuyipeng. Out of respect for the guest, people gave Bei Bei some food. Unexpectedly, the panda formed a habit and kept coming for food frequently. Experts worried that the panda might form a dependence and become just like a captive-bred panda. So, they captured the panda and released it in the mountain over 50 km away.

To their surprise, Bei Bei was back after 49 days. The moment the panda slipped into the Wuyipeng station, this rude animal started sniffing around and rummaging through boxes and cabinets, turning the tent into a complete mass. Everybody was driven out of the tent. With the panda's acute sense of smell, Bei Bei found bacon hidden on the beam of the kitchen, high off the ground. The panda twitched its nose, climbed to the top of the tent in an instant, sat on the beam, and started to eat the black smoked bacon while licking its lips. If pandas could speak, it would have said: "Excuse me. I am a carnivore in nature."

Pandas visiting folks are entertained with delicious meat bones.

LET ME HELP YOU

WUYIPENG STANDS HIGH
ON THE MOUNTAIN

May 14, 1980 was an important day in the history of protecting and studying giant pandas.

A group of people including the WWF President Peter Scott, together with his wife, and George Schaller, an authority in the research of Felidae (the cat family), accompanied by Professor Hu Jinchu and others, arrived at the Wolong Nature Reserve in Wenchuan County, Sichuan Province. Differing from other foreign expeditions for hunting and killing pandas decades ago, it was an expert team made up of caring people seeking to protect and study the giant panda.

The next day, they went into the mountains.

While the distant Balang Mountain was still covered by snow, the banks of the Pitiao River displayed numerous Spring flowers. The SUV stopped at the Wolong Pass, hosts and guests got off the car and began to walk. They negotiated a shaky chain bridge and started climbing along the zigzagging path.

More than an hour later, they finally got through the 36 twists of the rugged mountain path to reach a flat clearing surrounded by purple rhododendrons. On the edge of the bamboo grove, Hu Jinchu showed the guests a bamboo stump left by pandas after eating ago and fresh panda droppings.

Bonfire at Wuyipeng.

83

Schaller even knelt down, lifted some warm panda dung, comprising some pieces of spindle-shaped objects, and smelled them. He smiled: "Wow, there are some sweet scents from the newly trimmed grass." He gingerly handed over a piece of "spindle-shaped object" to Scott, who held it like a treasure and looked at it repeatedly. The rows of bamboo joints were glued together by mucus, indicating that pandas only absorbed limited nutrition.

Everyone laughed at the sight of the doctor and the English lord playing with panda dung.

Dr. Schaller said excitedly: "We have entered a panda kingdom!"

Among the tall and beautiful rhododendron groves, there were a few tents, which formed the Wuyipeng station. In March 1978, Professor Hu Jinchu, together with Zhou Shoude and Tian Zhixiang in Wolong, founded the wild observation station of giant pandas. Because there was a staircase of 51 steps between the camp and water source, the site was called Wuyipeng, meaning a station of 51 steps. Of especial interest to Schaller, there were seven 100-km-long observation lines marked with signals, centered on Wuyipeng. Only those who worked in the mountains and forests for a long time could know their importance: When you were exhausted, starving, drenched and losing your sense of direction, following an observation line would lead to "home", and a blazing fire, hot tea, delicious meals and warm beds.

Professor Hu Jinchu inspecting giant pandas in the wild.

At the panda feeding farm in Yingxionggou, Scott met with six month old panda. Looking at the WWF president, the honest little panda was not panicked or surprised, but a little shy, as if saying: "Hello, my old friend, so you've finally come!"

Everyone was fascinated by this little adorable panda.

Thanks to the field investigation, the WWF was keen to cooperate with China.

The WWF included giant pandas into the list of endangered rare animals in need of speedy rescue and granted millions of dollars to finance construction of the China Research and Conservation Center for the Giant Panda. The field observation station of Wuyipeng became a base for Sino-foreign cooperative research into wild giant pandas.

As part of the collaboration, the WWF dispatched an expert team led by George Schaller. The Chinese expert team was led by Hu Jinchu, with team members including Pan Wenshi from Peking University and Zhu Jing from the Chinese Academy of Sciences. Personnel from various nature reserves undertook field investigation following the Chinese and foreign experts.

The cooperation projects started in the winter of 1980, the coldest time in Wolong.

Every day, the expert team walked along an observation line. Sometimes, they groveled on their hands and knees in bamboo groves; sometimes they clambered up wisteria to look around and note traces of pandas. They measured the panda dung and eaten bamboos meticulously. In this way, while walking, the sweat and melt snow-water congregated together and froze the insulated cold weather clothing they wore. In the dusk, when people returned to Wuyipeng, they seemed to be clad in a thick ice armor, giving off a creaking noise while they walked.

▲ Sir Peter Scott (left) and Dr. George Beals Schaller are glad to find panda excrement.

▼ The Wolong Panda Center began to seek foreign cooperation in the 1980s: Zhou Shoude (first right), first chief of Wuyipeng.

◄ Dr. George Beals Schaller, and his Chinese counterparts - giant panda research experts Pan Wenshi (left) and Lu Zhi (middle) - conducting field inspection together.

On the morning of March 10, a panda was found in a cage trap and later named Zhen Zhen. Experts carried out a series of examinations and put a wireless neck strap around its neck after narcotizing it. Then the panda was released into the wild again. Afterwards, at Tangjiahe in Qingchuan County, the second Chinese-foreign cooperation base in Wolong, 15 pandas became research objects supplying much valuable information.

In 1986, *Wolong's Giant Panda*, a book showing the research achievements of Sino-foreign cooperation concerning giant pandas, was published in both Chinese and English and was recognized as the foundation of scientific research about the animals.

Thirty years have passed! When accounting for the scientific research achievements we respect those pioneers like Hu Jinchu, Dr. Schaller, Pan Wenshi and Zhu Jing even more!

Meanwhile, we'd also like to pay our respect to those research pandas! The wireless neck strap may cause great inconvenience to their survival, and some pandas even died because the neck weren't changed in time as they grew.

Wuyipeng: today and yesterday.

THE MOST
BEAUTIFUL RESERVE

On a moonlit night after the snow, cold silver light spread over the entire forest. The signal from the earphones grew louder and louder, indicating that the giant panda Pi Pi was coming closer to the 4X observation point. Zhang Hemin, the person in charge of the reserve, couldn't help opening the zipper of his tent. The moonlight, together with the freezing air, poured in and the tent seemed to be drowned in a sea of ice. Along with the rustling sounds from the fargesia groves, Pi Pi, as indicated by the wireless neck strap, was coming closer. What did it come for? Pi Pi had grabbed the rice cooker with its mouth and carried it off before Zhang Hemin could react. The panda sat under the fir tree in front of the tent and made a clean swallow of the rice in the cooker. That's it. Pi Pi had finished the food that should have lasted Zhang and his colleagues three days. Hence, they had to weather three days of cold and hunger in order to continue the recording of every 15 minutes.

4X, located at an altitude of over 3,000 meters, was a derived observation point of Wuyipeng. Its staff had vivid recollections of the blinding silver moonlight in which people starved and froze. The life in Wolong was impoverished and lonely.

It seemed that those 30 years passed in a flash. Zhang Hemin's team got bigger and became a shining banner in the world - the China Research and Conservation Center for the Giant Panda (CRCCGP or the Center for short). After a lot of hard work, the giant pandas at the

Center continued to give birth every year, and the number of captive-bred pandas has grown from 10 to 179 at present, or about 60 percent of the world's captive-bred pandas. Many famous pandas, such as Tuan Tuan and Yuan Yuan, the eight Olympic pandas, the 10 Expo pandas in Shanghai as well as the panda at the Asian Games held in Guangzhou, all came from the Center. The artificial feeding and breeding technologies of giant pandas have been exported to Europe, America and the Asia-Pacific region. The fascinating cries of panda babies have spread from overseas thanks to far-reaching international cooperation.

Success can only be achieved through numerous arduous efforts.

Zhang Hemin once held Ying Ying, a panda aged around two and weighing nearly 50 kg, and tried to put it onto a tree trunk. He was teaching Ying Ying how to climb trees and carrying out physical training. Ying Ying suddenly got mad after repeated exercises and bit Zhang on his left shank twice. Zhang Hemin's left trouser and shoe were both soaked in blood. The fierce pain made him clench the training stick in his hand even tighter. Ying Ying would relax its bite if hit mercilessly with the stick, but Zhang didn't do that. The bite left a deep wound on his shank, and he had to stay in hospital for three months due to the wound; his wife couldn't help shedding tears.

Talking of his wound, Zhang said: "It's hard work loving giant pandas." It is easy to become fascinated by the charmingly naive and cute pandas; however, as scientists, it means passion and perspiration, tears and suffering to fulfill the goals of the work.

"It's hard work loving giant pandas" became a pet phrase of panda scientific workers. After the Wenchuan earthquake on May 12, 2008, people from Wolong made the most brilliant interpretation of the phrase.

The panda home located in Hetaoping of the China Research and Conservation Center for the Giant Panda
(destroyed in the Wenchuan earthquake on May 12, 2008).

When the earthquake struck, Zhang Hemin was travelling back from a meeting in Chengdu and found the road blocked from Dujiangyan to Yingxiu Town. All of a sudden, he found himself facing a scene like something out of a Hollywood disaster movie, and all he could see were tragedies and disasters. Zhang was determined to press on, however, and finally reached Wolong where he braced himself for disaster.

The direct distance between Wolong and Yingxiu, the epicenter, was less than 10 km. Most of the animal housing was destroyed. The working staff at the center led 35 foreign tourists to safety, rescued 50 giant pandas, searching for and saving many who had run away in panic, such as Tuan Tuan, Yuan Yuan and Guo Guo, at risk of their own lives.

The Wenchuan earthquake destroyed the panda home located in Hetaoping, but the people in Gengda of Wolong Town gave up the ground where they had lived for many generations - Shenshuping to Huangcaoping - in order to provide a comfortable living environment for pandas in the disaster-stricken area. In 2013, a new Wolong base was completed. The villagers from Shiqiao Village, Qingchengshan Town, Dujiangyan City have lovingly taken in the settlement of the Giant Panda Rescue and Disease Control & Prevention Center. Together with the Ya'an Bifengxia Panda Base completed in 2003, the CRCCGP has formed the basic pattern of "one center, three bases", and has become the biggest, most advanced and reinforced conservation and research organization of giant pandas as well as the mother ship to protect pandas.

On November 20, 2013, a forum was held in Wolong to celebrate the 30th anniversary of CRCCGP's establishment. On that very day, smiles on the faces of Wolong people of three generations were even brighter than the Sun. The letter of congratulation written by Dr. David

◀ Pandas eating after the Wenchuan earthquake.

◥ Giant pandas being transferred to safe place soon after the earthquake.

Wilt, the director of the Species Conservation Center in the Smithsonian Conservation Biology Institute of National Zoological Park of America, was read out in public:

"As a scientist, I have traveled around the world in the last 30 years, and have the opportunity to work with the most competent wildlife conservation experts in the most beautiful nature reserves on the planet. I can say in earnest that no other nature reserve enjoys equal international reputation like CRCCGP because of the unique contribution Wolong has made in protecting giant pandas."

The moonlight in that year and the sunshine at the moment both turned into the sparkling tears in the eyes of Wolong people. There are so many beautiful mountains, rivers, pandas and people in Wolong!

Sixteen pandas bred in the China Research and Conservation Center for the Giant Panda of Wolong enjoy a rare sunny day on November 1, 2005.

Little pandas of the "kindergarten" of the Wolong Panda Base in February 2006.

CHENGDU
- METROPOLITAN CITY FOR PANDAS

Fargesia is the staple food of giant pandas that withers after blooming. The period between 1974 and 1976 was an age of starvation in the history of pandas. Among the rolling mountains, lots of fargesia bloomed and left blocks of brown stains on the ground. The mountains, with shroud of death spreading all over, looked as if had been burnt.

The investigation team from the Ministry of Forestry went to the Minshan Mountain range to investigate. The investigation team members had to trod through knee-deep snow, passing through bamboo groves that had withered and turned black and came across panda corpses one after another. Some of the bodies had already become utterly putrid while some had been torn to pieces by jackals and wolves. Some mothers and babies had fallen asleep in the snow valley and would never wake up again. The miserable images made the toughest men shed tears. The death toll was a bitter blow - 138 pandas in all.

Meanwhile, pandas falling ill because of hunger were sent to the Chengdu Zoo from different places until at one time there were 40 being cared for. Every panda was a mere bag of bones, and some were even too weak to chew. All of these panda had roundworms internally, including one with more than 3,000 roundworms.

◀ Chengdu Research Base of Giant Panda Breeding.

◁ Sculpture of a "giant panda" on the wall of the Chengdu International Finance Center.

Chengdu Research Base of Giant Panda Breeding.

In the summer of 1983, the disaster struck once again. Large tracks of arundhoriaalpha in the Minshan and Qionglai ranges began to bloom and wither again, and more than 500 pandas faced fresh starvation. The news shocked the world, and an upsurge of protecting pandas swept across the globe.

A song named *Panda Mimi* reproduced those unforgettable years:

The bamboos are blooming,

While Mimi is counting stars in its mum's arms,

Stars, sparkling stars, where is my breakfast for tomorrow?

Mimi, Mimi, trust us, we would never forget you....

Giant pandas were once prominent on the East Asian continent. During the past thousands of years, the range of human activities had expanded, destroying forests to reclaim land invaded and occupied the habitats of pandas especially after humankind developed an agriculture civilization, which made the living space of pandas ever smaller. Since the 1990s, China has completely forbidden cutting trees in the upstream region of Yangtze River, which actually protects the living environment of humans from floods but also helps protect the habitats of pandas.

Just as the song goes - "let me help you just like I help myself".

The Chengdu Zoo became the medical and rescue center for giant pandas again. Ninety percent of the pandas sent to Chengdu were saved. However, the recovered pandas couldn't be released into the wild because the ecological environment hadn't been restored. Therefore, the strategic thinking of ex-situ conservation came into being.

There is a world-renowned success profile in terms of ex-situ conservation: Chinese elks (commonly known as Father David's deer) once bred in the royal park located in Nanhaizi of Beijing. In 1866, Chinese elks were discovered by the Catholic Priest Father David

Visitors to the Chengdu Research Base of Giant Panda Breeding.

The Chengdu Research Base of Giant Panda Breeding, located in the Futou Mountain in the northern suburbs of Chengdu, replicates the natural environment for pandas in the wild, with tree and bamboo coverage reaching 96 percent of the area.

Panda babies practicing Kung Fu in the Base.

Armand and were believed to be a new species. David bought more than 20 elks and managed to transport them to Europe and to captive-breed them in the zoos. However, the elks bred in Nanhaizi later died out in China due to floods and warfare. After the outbreak of World War II, the British Duke of Bedford, who loved animals, was afraid that the war might bring disaster to the elks. He gathered 18 elks scattered across Europe and put them in the Woburn Abbey because of the rich grass and water sources there. Thus, the elks had received effective ex-situ conservation and even gradually increased in number. After 1985, a total of 39 elks that Britain provided free of charge came back to their homeland and were bred in Dafeng City of Jiangsu Province and Nanhaizi of Beijing. The elks have increased in number in the past 20 years, and the total in Dafeng City alone is 1,618 now. A species has been thus conserved and even flourished.

In 1987, the Chengdu Research Base of Giant Panda Breeding (hereinafter referred to as the Base) was constructed in a strategic town of ex-situ conservation. The location of the Base was the Futou Mountain, a shallow hill in the northern suburbs of Chengdu City. There was only a single bumpy motor road connecting it to the city.

The first-stage project was completed in only one year surprisingly. Hope started to sprout on the land of Shiguzi.

After 20 years of expansion, a panda eco-park, surrounded by trees, birds and flowers and with an area of 200 hectares, was formed. The corridors sheltered by green bamboos lead the tourist to one and another panda cottage. There are different toys for the pandas in front of the cottages as well as many soaring trees that offer excellent spots for pandas to indulge in climbing and sunbathing. Through the glass windows of the Sun Maternity Room and the Moon Maternity Room, the never-ending flow of tourists can witness lovely panda babies.

The number bred in the Base has grown from six in 1987 to 128 of four generations at present, taking up one-third of captive-bred pandas. Nowadays, pandas from the Base have settled in the

zoos in America, Spain, Canada and France in pairs. They have added to the joy and happiness of the world, and more and more people get the chance to enjoy the achievements of the Base.

During the past 20 years, more than 100 heads of State and foreign politicians, including the king of Sweden and the wife of the US president, as well as over 10 million domestic and foreign tourists have visited the Base and met the lovely giant pandas here. The United Nations has twice awarded the Base its Global 500 Roll of Honor for Environmental Achievement.

Chengdu has provided a success profile for the ex-situ conservation of giant pandas that were once an endangered species. The Capital of Pandas becomes a visiting card Chengdu hands out to the world.

Ex-Situ Conservation of Giant Pandas

According to the standards of the International Union for Conservation of Nature (IUCN), where the number of an endangered species declines to around 1,000 then humans should get involved, build an artificially simulated environment and carry out ex-situ conservation.

Up to now, China has divided the major habitats of giant pandas into 64 nature reserves covering in-situ conservation. Compared with in-situ conservation, ex-situ conservation refers to transferring giant pandas to artificial environments (like zoos or feeding farms) or another environment suitable for them to live in.

Spanish Queen of Spain Sofía de Grecia y Dinamarca visited the base on June 29, 2007.

On September 7, 2007, seven-year-old "boy" Bing Xin and four-year-old "girl" Huazuiba left the Base for Spain. Having a picture taken before the departure.

Governor-General of Australia Dame Quentin Alice Louise Bryce (middle) and her delegation having a picture taken with giant panda in the Chengdu Base on October 22, 2013.

FOUR SEASONS SONG
OF PANDA NANNIES

Pandas are famous around the world. However, panda nannies are unknown to the public.

"Chief nanny" Huang Xiangming of the Chengdu Research Base of Giant Panda Breeding said: "We work days and nights, without holidays. Our *Four Seasons Song* is about oestrus, mating, parturition and nursing of pandas."

March is the month when the winter Jasmine blooms, and also the time of panda oestrus. During the month, the pandas wander anxiously and rub their private parts against walls and trees from time to time, giving out bleating cries. Nannies will watch and record this period day and night. To improve the successful mating ratio, they must accurately grasp the time of mating or artificial insemination. Researchers conduct 24-hour monitoring of hormones in panda urine. Even if a female panda urinates at night, they will carefully collect it with a needle tube for immediate testing. Once they find the hormones (oestrogen and progesterone) have reached the best values, nannies will immediately arrange natural mating.

◀ Feeding the panda with nutritious steamed corn bread.

109

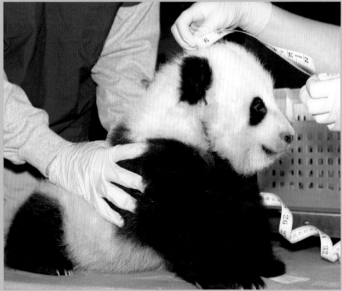

The technique is to let a male panda and a female panda approach each other. If there is an evident liking, a mating will be arranged. Interestingly, a number of over six-year-old male pandas will be organized to observe the mating process outside the "bridal chamber" to help them accumulate knowledge about the mating process.

In case of failure of natural mating, the male panda will be anesthetized to collect fresh sperm for artificial insemination of the female. In recent years, the pregnancy rate has been 100 percent due to a combination of natural mating and artificial insemination.

All nannies know individual differences mean not every female panda can give birth. Special care should be given to "primiparae" (first pregnancy). The urgent task is to train individual pandas to become qualified mothers.

After suffering pains, Jiao Zi gave birth to its first baby. It knew nothing about the red screaming object it had produced and was so scared it climbed onto the iron bars to flee.

Mei Mei's first issue was tossed aside, injuring the tiny cub.

However, after patient training, pandas such as Jiao Zi and Mei Mei have gradually learned how to be good mothers. Jiao Zi not only took good care of its twins, but also helped other mothers feed their babies. Later, Mei Mei was moved to Wakayama, Japan, where it gave birth to twins. Mei Mei, too, became a "hero mother" able to independently feed its offspring.

In 2008 in Wakayama, Liangbang gave birth to twins Meibang and Yongbang. Nanny Li Jia was dispatched to take care of them.

Liangbang is a daughter of celebrity mum Mei Mei, who was born in Japan. Thus, the arrival of its twins meant that Mei Mei's grandchildren were born in Japan. Japanese media and the public paid high attention to this event, making Li Jia very nervous. Unfortunately, the twins had something wrong with their digestive tracts, suffering diarrhea.

Li Jia fried rice in a pot, then ground it into powder, and finally mixed it with medicine. It fed the twins this mixture for seven or eight successive days until the diarrhea finally stopped. Li Jia said: "Panda babies are so small, and their mouths are even smaller, so it needs patience to prevent them from choking. It is much more difficult to feed panda babies than to feed human infants as they are as small as little mice".

From August and September to midwinter (more than 100 days after birth), nannies face the most difficult time in their work. Those on duty sit in front of the animal houses absolutely still like a stone.

They have to be very vigilant. They recorded every movement of the panda mothers in great detail, including leaning to one side, licking their panda babies, eating bamboo shoots and toilet movements. They will change the positions of twins quickly by distracting the attention of the mother with a basin of milk.

Nannies in the nursery clean panda babies with absorbent cotton regularly to encourage regular toilet habits. They nurse them with small bottles to provide supplementary nutrition. Then, they put them into warm incubators.

Pandas are sensitive to heat rather than cold. The oval-shaped delivery room is transparent and spacious, without any heating and air conditioning. In winter, with the arrival of cold wind and rain, duty nannies have to sit for at least four hours. In order to keep out the cold, they put on thick padded coats. They must record the mother's every movement and their babies' cry at any time. They worry that the mother may accidentally roll on top of a cub while napping, or the latter might fall down on the cold ground....

For nannies, it is more difficult than caring for their own children.

Panda nannies have to suffer hardships and high pressure. In addition, they often have to face difficult choices.

Lan Qiyuan was one of the first panda nannies. In the fall of 1990, her husband was hospitalized with two broken ribs. Besides, her daughter was giving birth herself. However, Lan Qiyuan did not give up her work and continued to take care of her pandas.

Due to few manpower to cope with a heavy workload, some pregnant nannies even continued to work. During night shift, Nanny Zuo Hong drank strong tea when she felt sleepy. Later, after giving birth, it was found that the excessive tea drinking had affected her baby's health.

Nanny Li Jia was busy in Wakayama for three months in 2008. Before returning home, Li Jia thought of Meibang and Yongbang from time to time, and cried sadly. She said it could not live without her beloved pandas.

Chen Min believed it had become simple and frank like its pandas after getting along with them for a long time. She said: "Family visits are not common for nannies. We work day and night because of hybridization and baby nursing. To take care of confined panda mums, we can't go home for several months. However, our family members sometimes come to see us."

For more than 20 years, the "family visit" has become part of the routine at the Panda Base.

Chen Min said: "One day, when I did go home, my five-year-old son was surprised and asked me why I had time to come back. He was so nice that he said: 'Panda babies need you.' In his mind, I belong to the panda babies. I could not help bursting into tears while hugging the little boy."

Generations of panda nannies dedicate themselves to the undertaking throughout their life. Their eyes are full of love and expectation. On behalf of humankind, they accompany the giant pandas, waiting for the revival of the endangered species.

Panda nannies are indeed ordinary but noble!

A wrestling match

VIDEO

114

HEARTBREAKING
XIANG XIANG

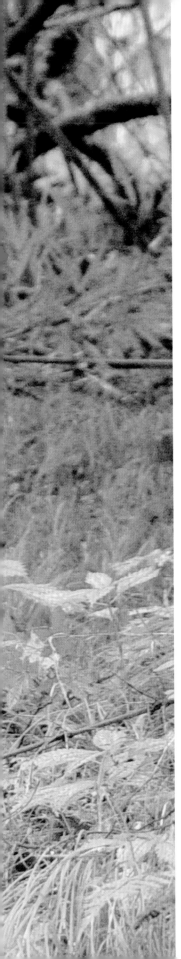

On the night of July 16, 2005, some people were drinking beer on the river bank of Dujiangyan City. They suddenly spotted a shadow moving on a roof. They shouted, mistaking it was a thief. The shadow moved rapidly, and climbed onto a tree. It was then they realized it was a panda.

Its appearance in the downtown area excited local people and a large "rescue" campaign was launched. The panda was so frightened it hid and finally jumped into the river; however, it struggled ashore and climbed onto a tree. On July 17, experts from the Wolong Nature Reserve and forest fire officers came to the rescue.

This tree was located on the river bank. Because of worry about it falling into the river, the Dujiangyan, flowing for millennia, was diverted for two hours. Firefighters laid thick mattresses, and finally helped it get down, disregarding its scratching and biting.

Experts analyzed that the panda had just left its mother, and got lost in the Zhaogong Mountain area. Flashing headlights made it scared. It ran away along the hillside, and finally reached the downtown area and climbed up onto the house roof.

◁ Giant panda Xiang Xiang.

◁ Xiang Xiang being released into the wild.

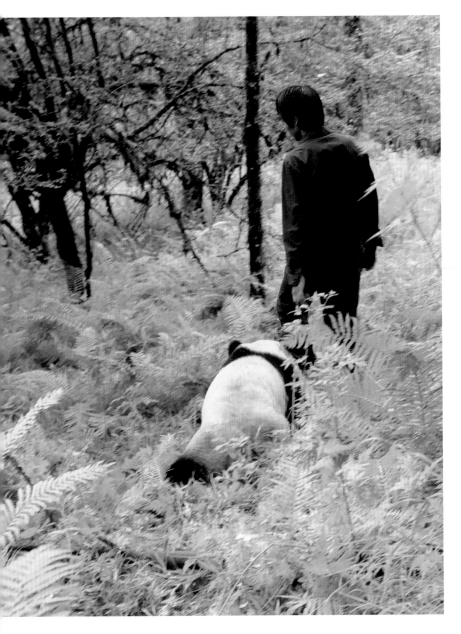

Xiang Xiang receiving training.

After thorough physical examination and recuperation in Wolong, it was named Shenglin No.1 and equipped with a wireless neck strap. In more than 20 days of comfortable life, it gradually established close relationships with the breeding staff. On August 8, balloons rose in the Wolong Giant Panda Protection Center, to say farewell to "Shenglin No.1". One slogan expresses the wish of the Wolong people:

"Shenglin No.1, take care of yourself in the wild!"

After successful exploration about captive-bred pandas, researchers began to study a combination of in-situ and ex-situ conservation. Captive-bred pandas are returned to nature after field training to ensure they can participate in reproduction to achieve revival of the panda species.

Shenglin No.1's return to nature is only a prelude of wild release. The program still has a long way to go.

On July 8, 2003, when over two years old, Xiang Xiang, the world's first captive giant panda involved in the field training study, was moved to the native habitat lying at an altitude of 2,080 meters and covering an area of 27,000 square meters.

However, Xiang Xiang, being accustomed to eating a "ready-cooked" meal, did not know how to find food. Every day, it waited for the whistle of research personnel. Once hearing footsteps, it would pass through the bamboo forest and run over to ask for food.

Researchers gradually reduced the supply, and guided it to find fargesia robusta, polygonatum odoratum in the Emei Mountain, along with other rich food resources. At first, it wasted much fresh and tender bamboo tips. Later, it gradually learned to collect and eat half withered bamboo, perennial bamboo and nutrient-rich bamboo leaves. It finally solved the problem of eating, and had the ability to survive independently.

On September 15, 2004, Xiang Xiang was moved to the phase-II field-training circle at an altitude of 2,480 meters and with a total area of 240,000 square meters. It gradually became wild, and even screamed at its breeder Liu Bin.

After nearly three years of training, Xiang Xiang increased its weight to 95.2 kg, and its body conditions were better than other pandas of the same age. On April 28, 2006, it was released to the forest. After a night of heavy rain, the bamboo became brighter in the morning.

On a platform full of Fargesia nitida in the jungle of the Dengsheng Observation Station of the Wolong Natural Reserve, over 100 people including officials, scholars and journalists from across the country already gathered to see off Xiang Xiang.

At the end of the ceremony, the cage was opened. Xiang Xiang suddenly got excited and rushed off into the bamboo forest. Journalists found breeder Liu Bin's eyes had turned red. Zhang Hemin choked with emotion when speaking to them.

Xiang Xiang released into the wild on April 28, 2006 after the training.

Xiang Xiang's death saddened research staff. After summary, experts think that, although Xiang Xiang received field training, it was inferior to pandas born in the wild and which have rich experience of fighting. In addition, Wuyipeng is a compact district of pandas. The competition for nest domain is rather intense. Xiang Xiang, as a newcomer, must have encountered collective resistance.

However, Xiang Xiang's death did not stop the program.

Wild Pandas

According to the Third National Giant Panda Survey results released in 2004, there were a total of 1,590 giant pandas in the wild. The fourth survey was launched on October 25, 2011, and lasted over two years. The results have yet to be released. But surveyors' professional dedication to track giant pandas despite many hardships will write a splendid chapter in the history of giant panda research.

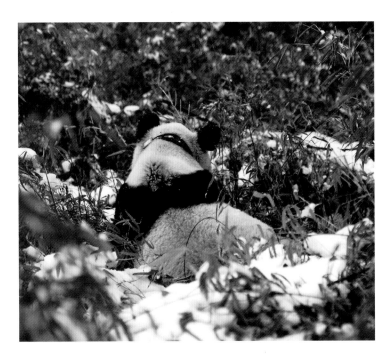

◀ Xiang Xiang enjoying a free life in the wild.

▲ Xiang Xiang got injured.

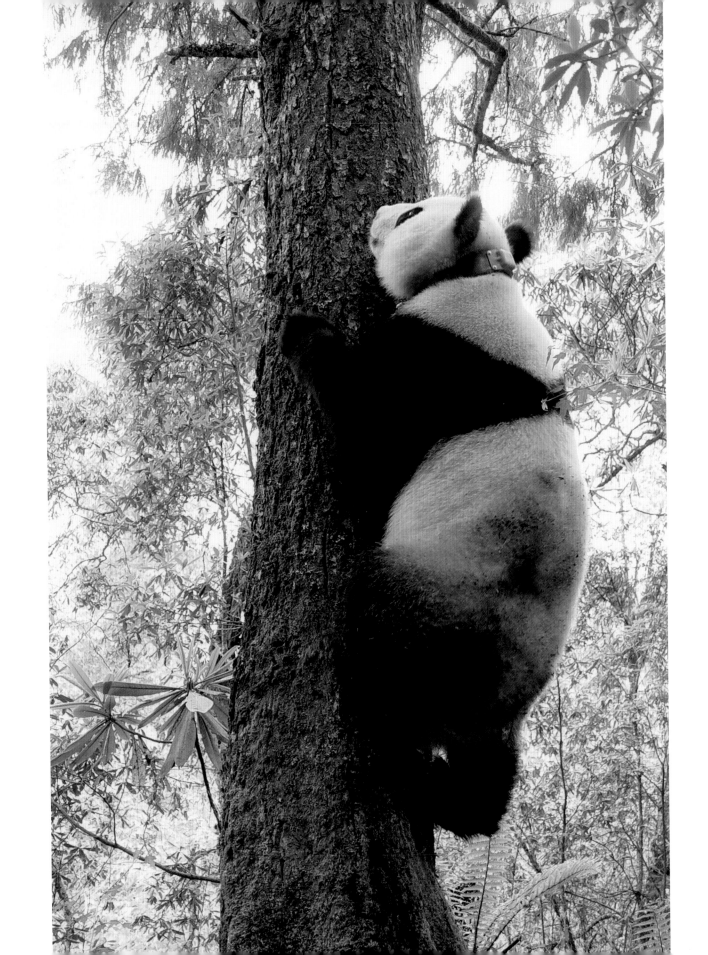

However, on December 13, Xiang Xiang departed from normal behavior, and moved a long distance. On December 22, 2006, researchers managed to find Xiang Xiang eating bamboo through the cage. It displayed serious injuries to its back, hind limb and palm.

After sedating Xiang Xiang, ambulance men carried it to Wuyipeng, where they conducted wound debridement, suturing and bandaging, while letting the panda eat enough bamboo shoots and bamboo. Because of worry that too long treatment would make it dependent on people once again, Xiang Xiang was released into the Baiyan area near the field observation station of Wuyipeng on December 30.

On January 7, 2007, Xiang Xiang's neck strap gave out quite weak signal that disappeared later. On the afternoon of February 19, searchers found the dead Xiang Xiang on snow-covered Zhuanjinggou. Anatomy results show that Xiang Xiang had got involved in a fierce fight with wild pandas, and had fallen off a cliff. Left thoraco-abdominal deformation, tissue injuries, and severe injury to the pancreas, caused its death.

◀▶ Xiang Xiang enjoying a free life in the wild.

Experts selected Cao Cao to follow after Xiang Xiang on the release program.

Cao Cao was discovered in the wild in Wolong when only six months old; it was alone facing high winds and snow. For care, it was sent to the China Research and Conservation Center for the Giant Panda (CRCCGP).

Fortunately, Cao Cao had grasped the skill of climbing trees, which is not owned by many captive-bred pandas, and this valuable experience can be passed to its offspring.

On July 20, 2010, pregnant Cao Cao entered the first field-training circle in the forest with an elevation of 1,780 meters and covering an area of 2,400 square meters. Cameras were installed on walls and trees around the circle for the purpose of observing Cao Cao at any time. A delivery room was also set up for its parturition.

However, Cao Cao didn't like the artificial delivery room. On a rainy night in August, it gave birth to a healthy baby in the grass nest. Its cry was loud enough to deter small beasts readying to attack.

◀ Tao Tao in the snow-covered wilds.

◀ Cao Cao and its child.

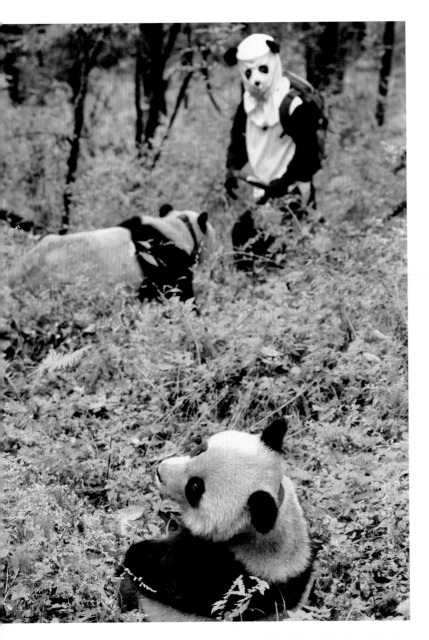

On October 7, 2012, Tao Tao was to be released to the wild after being trained to survive there.

It was raining heavily. Looking at the drenched Cao Cao and baby on their monitor screen, experts were distressed.

Director Zhang Hemin told journalists later: "Wild pandas rest in tree holes, but Cao Cao and its baby had nothing. We wanted to help them. But considering all previous efforts might be wasted, we finally decided not to intervene. After all, it is the first experiment. "

Results show that it was an unnecessary worry. Cao Cao and its cub were fine. Cao Cao protected the youngster with its arms and warmed it. Panda fur can keep an animal very warm. Even if a panda sleeps on the snow for one night in winter, no melting will be apparent the next day.

The new sub was Tao Tao. Seven days later, Tao Tao changed in color, and its ears and limbs became light black. A month later, it had basically grown to look like a real panda, with a pair of black eyes. On the 35th day after birth, Tao Tao opened its eyes for the first time.

To ensure Tao Tao could return to the wild state, researchers adhered to the principle of preventing contact with people. Therefore, the work of regularly checking physical condition and adjusting the monitoring facilities must be done by Pandamen dressed in black and white plush suits and helmets to look exactly like fat panda mothers. The key is that they carried the urine and smell of Cao Cao, so Tao Tao could feel familiar. The Pandamen helped Cao Cao and Tao Tao in the circle move two times, and provided supplementary nutrition to the youngster.

Through the monitor, researchers, however, witnessed some scary scenarios:

It was very sunny that day. Montains bathed in sunlight were so colorful and beautiful. Internationally famous documentary master Douglas Brown, with assistants carrying much equipment, looked especially excited. He was making a film entitled *Human Age of Earth*. The return of pandas to nature would play the key role in the story.

In the context of successful ex-situ conservation, more than 300 captive-bred pandas, and start of the wild-release program, the song popular 30 years ago is even more meaningful:

Let me help you, just like I help myself.

The world will become more beautiful....

Distribution of Giant Pandas

Giant pandas inhabit six major mountains - Minshan at the western margin of the Sichuan Basin, Qionglai, Liangshan, Daxiangling, Xiaoxiangling and southern rim of the Qinling Range in Shaanxi Prvince, stretching across 45 counties (cities) in Sichuan, Shaanxi and Gansu Provinces. The habitat area is more than 20,000 square km, with a panda population of about 1,600; about 80 percent of these are distributed in Sichuan Province. They prefer cols, ditches, hillsides, terraces and valleys, etc., and generally live in the slope zones with the temperature of below 20 degrees Centigrade for the convenience of seeking food and drinking water.

Panda Tao Tao.

VIDEO

When Zhang Xiang was a child.

What was that coveting Tao Tao? It is like a squirrel, but is much larger and fatter. It is a Paguma larvata (type of civet cat!) It popped its head in and looked about, carefully climbed off the tree, and approached the sleeping Cao Cao and sub step by step. Danger! Nervous researchers wanted to immediately drive away the terrible killer, being so nervous. But just when paguma larvata was only one or two meters away from Tao Tao, Cao Cao woke up suddenly and roared, which frightened the predator away.

One time, Tao Tao fell off a high tree, so Pandamen immediately set out, wanting to help. However, they found Tao Tao had climbed onto another tree...

In fact, it had grasped the skill of curling when falling down to avoid injury.

In the larger second field-training circle at a higher altitude, the group experienced mudslides, snowstorms and torrential rain.

Cao Cao, the careful mum, taught Tao Tao how to find water, how to shelter from the snow, and how to select bamboo not covered by snow.

The third field-training circle, tucked away at an elevation of 2,100-2,380 meters and covering an area of 240,000 square meters, was the typical habitat of wild giant pandas.

In the third circle, Cao Cao and Tao Tao encountered leopards for the first time. Adult pandas are not afraid of leopards, and will immediately climb a tree on smelling the odor of leopard dung. When meeting other pandas, Tao Tao behaved just like all the wild pandas, who only stare at each other from a distance.

On October 11, 2012, handsome and strong Tao Tao wearing a wireless neck strap, was released in Liziping, Shimian County, Ya'an City.

On November 6, 2013, another panda, Zhang Xiang, was also released after wild training in Wolong.

◀ Tao Tao quickly disappeared into the wild soon after the release.

Cao Cao training its child Tao Tao to climb a tree.

EVERYONE
LOVES PANDAS

RUTH AND HER SU LIN

Ruth and Su Lin moving down the aircraft.

The amazing discovery of Armand David in 1869 had an unfortunate side effect - the sounds of shots could be heard in the forests of western Sichuan.

The panda skin displayed in the National Museum of Natural History in Paris proved very tempting. Western explorers swarmed into the Chinese province in a competition to hunt pandas.

When the British Museum and the Chicago Museum had their first panda specimens, Western countries in general developed a desire to obtain live not dead pandas. It was a fashion designer who knew nothing about adventure, Ruth Elizabeth Harkness, who became the first person to take live pandas back to the United States.

In February 1936, her explorer husband died in Shanghai, and two months later she arrived in China to take back his ashes. She was determined to satisfy her husband's unfulfilled wish and capture pandas in western Sichuan. She got much support from a young Chinese, Yang Kunting, an accomplished linguist. They directly went to the Caopo (Grass Slope) in Wenchuan County of Sichuan.

Su Lin warmly received in the United States.

On the morning of November 9, 1936, it had stopped snowing. Hearing Yang Kunting calling her, Ruth quickly climbed onto the snowy slope. Once entering the bamboo forest, she heard a cry similar to that of a baby. And, indeed, it was a panda cub that Yang Kunting handed her.

They named the baby after Yang's sister-in-law, "Su Lin". The cub was less than two months old. It had not opened its eyes, but had developed the familiar black and white. The mother, it seemed, had been scared off, and the cub was hiding in a tree hole.

Ruth's arms were so warm. Su Lin scratched, and her toothless mouth rubbed against the woman's nipples making her feel itchy and numb as if she were suffering an electric shock. She stumbled back to the camp, and took out a feeding bottle and milk powder as any mother might do.

Although Su Lin was drinking milk for the first time, it held the feeding bottle in its arms very adeptly, which made Ruth laugh. Her flannel shirt, cashmere sweater and skirt, were torn up to make diapers, showing the confusion of the inexperienced would-be explorer.

Local people made a wicker basket for Su Lin, and eventually the cub was moved from China to the United States. The Adventure Club in New York, which until then had only allowed men to join, welcomed Ruth and Su Lin, less than half year old, as if receiving a head of State.

Celebrities including Theodore and Kermit Roosevelt, sons of the former US President Teddy Roosevelt, visited Su Lin. They were well known because of having once shot a giant panda at the same time. Ruth had closely studied the 1929 book written by Theodore Roosevelt Jr., *Trailing the Giant Panda*.

Theodore Roosevelt touched the furry Su Lin, and his eyes were full of love and affection. Brut Doran and Dean Sage, two others who had once hunted giant pandas in China, also arrived, hoping to hug Su Lin.

Su Lin, like a gentle baby, blinked its black eyes and quietly looked at the strangers. Its two round ears, like two big black velvet flowers, were a delight. Asked how he felt with Su Lin in his arms, Theodore Roosevelt said after a long time of silence: "I would rather kill my son than this little cute guy."

Sage observed: "We might commit crimes out of curiosity. I will not shoot giant panda any longer. "

On February 18, 1937, after sufficient preparation, Su Lin finally appeared before the public in the Chicago Zoo, to a record opening day crowd of 53,000 people.

To find a companion for lonely Su Lin, Ruth returned to China. After three months of hard trekking in Wenchuan, she finally found a panda which they later named Mei Mei, and took it back to the United States.

But her sense of accomplishment was suddenly shattered. On April 1, 1938, Su Lin died of acute pneumonia, having lived in the United States for only about a year. Ruth could not believe it. She was heartbroken.

To find a companion for Mei Mei, Ruth now had to return to China for the third time. She bought a panda cub, but for various reasons released it.

An Englishman named Floyd Tangier Smith was extremely dissatisfied with Ruth's "early achievement" and he spent a dozen years living in western Sichuan to capture 12 live pandas, although six died on the way to Britain.

Ruth Harkness often thought of the sentence: "Curiosity might bring disasters to the world."

Even alcohol didn't help ease the pain of losing Su Lin. On July 20, 1947, she died in the bathtub of a hotel in Pittsburgh, at the age of 46. Nobody knew whether she died for guilt.

On October 29, 2002, her casket was taken by her grandniece to China for burial on the Caopo (Grass Slope) where Ruth and Su Lin met for the first time.

Lifespan of the Giant Panda

Giant pandas can live for more than 20 years in the wild, and captive-bred giant pandas can live for over 30 years. One female giant panda in the Wuhan Zoo lived for 37 years, the longest lifespan so far.

VIDEO

Finally look at the camera

MEMORIES ABOUT HUAXIBA

图书在版编目（C I P）数据

熊猫的故事 : 画册 : 英文 / 谭楷著 ; 关威威译 . -- 北京 : 五洲传播出版社, 2014.12

ISBN 978-7-5085-3007-9

I . ①熊… II . ①谭… ②关… III . ①大熊猫—画册 IV . ① Q959.838-64

中国版本图书馆 CIP 数据核字 (2014) 第 285277 号

出 版 人　荆孝敏

科 学 顾 问　胡锦矗　张泽钧

撰　　　稿　谭　楷

翻　　　译　关威威

译　　　审　王国振　Michael Geoffrey Murray（英）

策 划 编 辑　王　莉

责 任 编 辑　王　莉　吴娅民

图 片 组 稿　谭　楷

图 片 提 供　（个人按姓名汉语拼音为序）

　　　程岩 费立松 高富华 高华康 衡毅 胡锦矗 黄万波 黄祥明 金勘琪 兰景超 李明喜 李伟 梁晓华 吕植 罗小韵 马亦生

　　　蒲涛 尚建华 佘轶 谭楷 王磊 王鹏彦 吴先智 向素珍 熊柏泉 杨老丹 雍严格 张金国 周孟棋 朱启良 卓玛

　　　Richard Jones（英） CFP 《大熊猫》杂志 台北市立动物园等

装 帧 设 计　丰饶文化传播有限责任公司

视 频 支 持　中国网络电视台熊猫频道（www.ipanda.com）

熊猫的故事

出 版 发 行　五洲传播出版社

地　　　址　北京市海淀区北三环中路 31 号生产力大楼 B 座 7 层

邮　　　编　100088

发 行 电 话　010-82007837 / 82001477 / 82005927

制　　　版　北京杰诚雅创文化传播有限公司

印　　　刷　北京市雅迪彩色印刷有限公司

开　　　本　787×1092mm 1/12

印　　　张　17.5

版　　　次　2015 年 2 月第 1 版第 1 次印刷

书　　　号　ISBN 978-7-5085-3007-9

定　　　价　358.00 元

The mayor accompanied Luo Weixiao to visit Father David's residence. When standing by the window, the public and visitors in the street cheered loudly and the local chorus sang the local folk song for welcoming distinguished guests. At the warm welcoming ceremony in the town with a history of over 1,000 years, Luo Weixiao shouted loudly while waving his fists: "I am coming, Ezpeleta!"

When donating the map covered all over with its postmarks to the National Museum of Natural History in Paris, Luo Weixiao told a journalist: "The giant pandas connect China with France and the rest of the world. Nowadays, the Jiajinshan Giant Panda Base in my hometown has been recognized as a world natural legacy. I revisited David's residence to thank him for his introduction of giant pandas to the world. I hope to spread the Chinese image of peace and friendship symbolized by pandas to the world."

In November 2014, the former mayor of Ezpeleta having a picture taken with his "adopted daughter" David in the Bifengxia Giant Panda Base in Ya'an.

At Dengchigou, three Catholic fathers prayed for him and the Consul General of France in Chengdu saw him off. When bidding farewell to him, all his friends felt sad.

Regardless of the weather, he must ride more than 100 km every day. He suffered a lot during the journey including changing the inner tubes five times and outer tires three times. Due to exposure to hot sunlight, his arms were badly sunburnt.

Dramatically, when being caught by Polish police for entering an expressway, he smilingly showed them the journey map marking the route, the postmarks of countries and cities through which he had passed, and the panda photos, which won police respect.

His journey was known in France. During the last stages, France's TV Station 3 followed him and newspapers praised him as a "cultural knight of pandas".

On July 10, Andre Derraidou, the former mayor of Ezpeleta, who had led the delegation of "David's friends" to visit Baoxing County three times, welcomed Luo Weixiao. They hugged with warm tears streaming down their faces.

"Giant Panda Culture Knight" Luo Weixiao cycles to Ezpeleta of France, hometown of Armand David.

Get together
for fans

VIDEO

At 5 a.m., Washington citizen Barbara Barron, a real panda lover, waited in line at the zoo. She told a journalist: "Bao Bao is so cute that I want to give her a big hug only for one second. I wish her to have a long and happy life."

On the same day, US First Lady Michelle Obama, together with the US State Department and many Americans, issued birthday wishes for Bao Bao on social network sites.

In China, there are also such thousands of panda lovers such as retired worker Luo Weixiao.

The 64-year-old is a member of the Sichuan Giant Panda Eco-culture Research Association, and also the hard-core godfather among cycling friends. With the bike, he has traveled across the Chinese Mainland and climbed onto the Qinghai-Tibet Plateau through four different routes.

The year of 2014 is the 145th anniversary of discovering giant pandas by Father Armand David, and also the 50th anniversary of establishing Sino-French diplomatic relations. On March 17, Luo Weixiao rode from Dengchigou Church to Ezpeleta in the southwest corner of France, the hometown of Armand David. The 15,000-km journey covered eight countries.

On October 10, 2014, some 500 adorable pet "pandas" appeared in Nanning, Guangxi Zhuang Autonomous Region, to arouse the general public to show care and concern for animals on verge of distinction.

Ming (below) and Chi Chi (above) deeply loved by the British.

Later, Zhang Zhihe asked them to rest under a tree, letting breeders take out several panda babies only about six months old, for the purpose of accompanying them. Several fluffy babies rolled over, wrestled and played, making them laugh. The old man said: "This is the happiest day in my life! "

The old couple enjoyed themselves only left the base at dusk. Staff lining up watched them go, with tears in their eyes. They all knew that he would not come again. He wanted to cherish and retain the final joy brought by pandas before passing away.

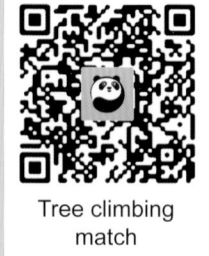

VIDEO

Tree climbing
match

GIANT PANDA
TRAVELERS TO JAPAN

As early as 685, Wu Zetian, the sole female emperor in Chinese history, sent a pair of pandas to Emperor Temmu of Japan as a gift, which was recorded in the *Japanese Imperial Yearbook*. That is to say, as early as 1,300 years ago, the envoy of friendship had sailed across the storms and high seas escorting our lovely pandas to Japan.

On October 28, 1972, when the private plane carrying Lan Lan and Kang Kang as a gift from China to Japan flew over Japanese territory, fighters of the Japanese Self-Defense Forces provided an escort just like heads of State.

A panda mania spread all over Japan. In the Ueno Zoo, people lined up to see Lan Lan and Kang Kang every day. However, with so many people anxious for a view, each person only got 30 seconds to linger in front of the pandas. If people happened to visit when pandas were having their afternoon nap, they would have to wait patiently.

However, it was a great pity that Lan Lan died on September 4, 1979. At that very moment at midnight, TV news programs showed Komori, the directing breeder at the Ueno Zoo, announcing the death with tremulous voice and tears in his eyes.

For several days after Lan Lan's death, tens of thousands of Japanese people wore black armbands, left flowers, fruit and funeral orations at the zoo to express their condolences.

► On April 1, 2011, a large number of Japanese people swarmed to Tokyo's Ueno Zoo to see the pandas.

► Poster showing giant pandas in Tokyo's Ueno Zoo.

In 1983, large areas of bashania fangiana in the Minshan Mountain and Qionglai Mountain began to bloom and wither, which threatened the survival of more than 500 wild pandas. Activities to rescue pandas were launched around Japan, and 19 Toyota SUV of bashania fangiana and more than 20 million Yen were sent to China. In September 1984, the Sichuan Wildlife Conservation Association held exhibitions concerning the panda rescue in Hiroshima, Fukuyama, Okayama and other cities of Japan; in Hiroshima alone, there were more than 20,000 visitors.

Afterwards, the panda exchange between China and Japan became more frequent. In the autumn of 1986, Huan Huan gave birth in the Ueno Zoo successfully, which added to the jubilant atmosphere prevailing in the whole country. The Ueno Zoo then selected a name with the same pronunciation and writing in both Chinese and Japan from among tens of thousands of names submitted: "Tong Tong".

On August 16, 2014, Tokyo's Ueno Zoo celebrated the 9th birthday of male panda Li Li.

Japanese businessmen quickly saw an opportunity and a panda toy was quickly marketed. Children could open the zipper on the belly of the panda mother to take out a panda baby with pleasant cries. It was a best seller then.

In the 1990s, China and Japan carried out deeper cooperation in terms of panda-related scientific research. In September 2003, Mei Mei gave birth to a pair of twins in Wakayama, Japan. Compared with Qing Qing whose twins had to be partly raised by staff, Mei Mei provided all the care herself and the babies quickly grew, vivacious and healthy. Mei Mei and family became the famous stars among Japanese people and were regarded as excellent goodwill ambassadors.

On July 24, 2011, the Japanese Government and the local government of Wakayama awarded three pandas in the Wakayama Shirahama Animal Park.

Two giant panda cubs in Japan's Wakayama Shirahama Safari Park.

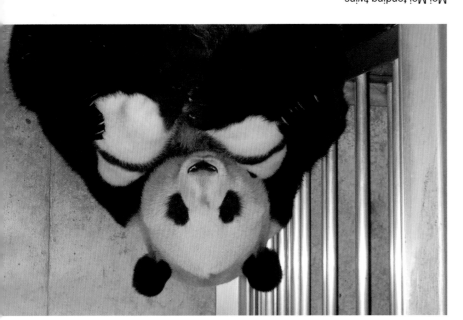

Mei Mei tending twins.

Japanese girl giving blessings to giant pandas ready to leave for China.

On October 28, 2007, twin giant pandas born in Japan warmly welcomed on their safe return to Chengdu.

The three pandas are the research members of the Chengdu Research Base of Giant Panda Breeding and the Shirahama Animal Park, including Liangbang who gave birth to a pair of panda twins in August 2010, Yongming who was father of the twins, as well as Mei Mei who had given birth to 10 panda babies in China and Japan but died three years before.

According to the Chengdu Research Base of Giant Panda Breeding, the China-Japan international science and research cooperation on giant pandas began in 1994. As of 2010, giant pandas sent to Japan had successfully given birth to 13 cubs in seven pregnancies in Japan, of whom 11 survived. At the foot of the Wakayama Mountain lies the biggest artificial breeding population of giant pandas outside China.

Japanese people have their own favorites. They visit their beloved pandas regularly and even persist for several years.

On October 28, 2007, Longbang and Qiubang, the twin pandas born in Japan, came back to China. When they left in the morning, it was raining heavily, but the fans ran after the cars and called their names in tears. Ten diehard fans even flew to Chengdu with Longbang and Qiubang and only departed after seeing them settled in their new home.

SHOCK WAVE BROUGHT
BY TAIWAN PANDA
BABY 'YUAN ZAI'

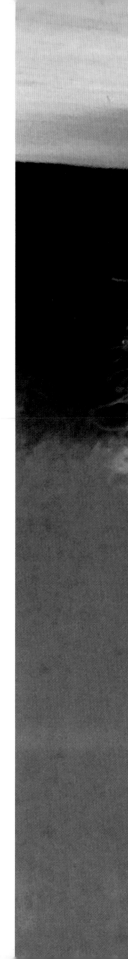

At 8: 02 p.m., July 6, 2013, Yuan Yuan, a giant panda in the Taipei Zoo, gave birth to a panda baby named Yuan Zai weighing 183.4 grams, meeting the expectations of millions of people. The birth put the clock back 30 years and pages on websites, magazines and newspapers were all instantly lit up by the news, and creating an exciting drama with many ups and downs.

When Yuan Yuan gave birth to Yuan Zai, Chen Yuyan with the Panda House was at the airport welcoming the "midwife" Wei Ming from the CRCCGP where Yuan Yuan had been raised.

Wei Ming has been engaged in panda baby delivery and nursing for 13 years, being the panda baby-sitter for more than 100 panda babies. As soon as he entered the Panda House, he threw down the luggage, donned a sterilized uniform and walked directly into the delivery room. Then he lay on his stomach to carefully observe every small movement of Yuan Yuan and the newborn cub. No abnormal phenomenon was found. However, six hours later, Wei Ming noticed that the hind legs of the offspring could not move naturally. When Yuan Yuan licked it, the baby cried particularly loudly. With years of experience, Wei Ming finally found a two-centimeter wound in the inner side of Yuan Zai's leg.

The wound was caused by the "disordered haste" haste of the mother in trying to hold the baby in her mouth; however, she dropped it, and then grabbed it with her paws. Obviously, Yuan Yuan still lacked the experience to be a careful mother.

The sensational story began:

Yuan Yuan needed to be separated from her daughter for a period of time to learn to be a mother as soon as possible. Meanwhile, poor Yuan Zai had to undergo a wound closure operation although Yuan Zai was less than one day old. During the operation without anesthetic treatment, how would Yuan Zai cope? With paper-thin and tender skin, how could the operation be performed? And how to stitch up the wound? Fortunately, eight days later, the wound healed well.

Yuan Zai, of course, could not do without mother's colostrum even for a day. The panda's colostrum is in light green like vegetable juice, rich in the necessary natural antibiotics baby pandas need to survive.

Dong Li, a young Tibetan man from the Aba Tibetan Autonomous Prefecture in Sichuan, bold but cautious, is a master hand in milking with 14 years of experience. He went to the Taipei Zoo to maintain close contact with Yuan Yuan as a visitor from her "home town". With an assistant of Taipei Zoo distracting Yuan Yuan's attention, Dong Li, sometimes crawling on the ground, sometimes lying alongside Yuan Yuan and was able to touch her nipples. Unlike other panda mums with four or six nipples, Yuan Yuan had five. For the first time, with sweat streaming off him, Dong Li milked 10 milliliters of precious colostrum.

Wei Ming, using his slender and warm hands, let the milk slowly

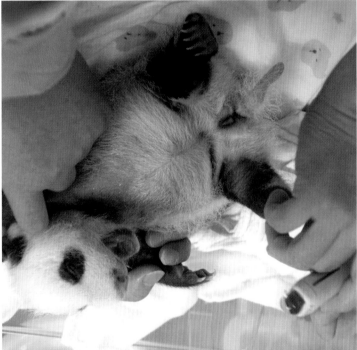

On August 4, 2013, Yuan Zai, the first giant panda born in Taiwan, was 30 days old, attracting many visitors.

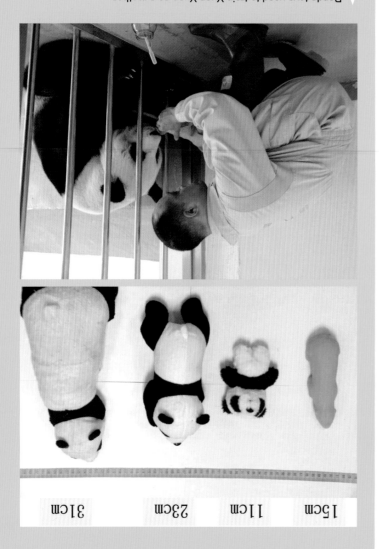

15cm　11cm　23cm　31cm

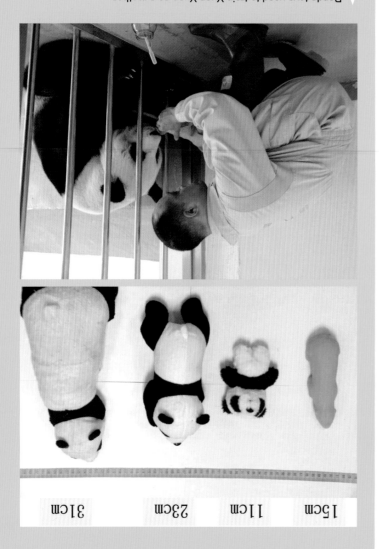

▲ Panda toys used to train Yuan Yuan as a mother.

▲ Breeding expert Dong Li gathering first milk for Yuan Yuan.

soak the lip of little Yuan Zai. The panda baby started to lick. The newborn cub could only drink 0.5-1 milliliters at a time, but had six to eight feedings each day. In 51 working days, Wei Ming slept at the Panda House for 46 days and nights.

Chen Yuyan and her colleagues accompanied and guarded the panda mother and baby day and night. Their eyes like tireless cameras, observed the change of Yuan Zai's fur color every minute. On the third day, the fur color around the eye socket turned dark; on the fourth day, the color of ears grew darker; on the seventh day, the color of shoulder and limbs became darker... the newborn mouse-like Yuan Zai gradually appeared as a true "cute and innocent" panda.

After Yuan Zai was taken away, Yuan Yuan irritably looked for her baby everywhere. What? A little one was squirming on the ground with the smell of baby's urine and the voice of "uhn na uhn na". The sharp-nosed Yuan Yuan decisively bit the panda baby and held the little one in her mouth.

The workers keeping watch via the TV monitor could not help cheering quietly.

In fact, it was a silicone doll like Yuan Zai, but it was sufficiently real for Yuan Yuan mistakenly regard it as its real baby. It helped Yuan Yuan to learn how to hold the baby in the mouth and how to hug it. Through a bluetooth device, workers controlled the cry of the doll outside of the cage to make Yuan Yuan continuously change

Yuan Zai finally seeing its mother Yuan Yuan.

Yuan Yuan and Yuan Zai.

the way of hugging the baby. Most fantastically, the doll's belly was equipped with not only a thermometer to measure the temperature when mother panda hugged it, but also two eggs! This means, if panda baby was held in the mouth too lightly, the baby would fall down; if too hard, the baby would be hurt. After repeated experiments, when the doll Yuan Zai was open, the eggs in its belly were intact, indicating that Yuan Yuan could perfectly hold the baby in its mouth.

Zhang Zhihua, secretary of the Taipei Zoo, said: "We dared not take any risk because we could not afford a failure. Thus, every step should be absolutely safe."

After 31 days of separation, Yuan Yuan finally was going to meet her real baby. All the personnel were worried and held their breath.

Chen Yuyan used a towel as a cushion, and put Yuan Zai, whose weight had reached 1,200 grams in front of the guardrails of the cage. The smell and the cry of Yuan Zai had distracted Yuan Yuan pacing back and forth in the cage. When Yuan Yuan came closer, Chen Yuyan carefully handed over Yuan Zai. At that moment, the excited Yuan Yuan happily cried, put her long tongue out of the guardrails, and constantly licked her beloved daughter who had been

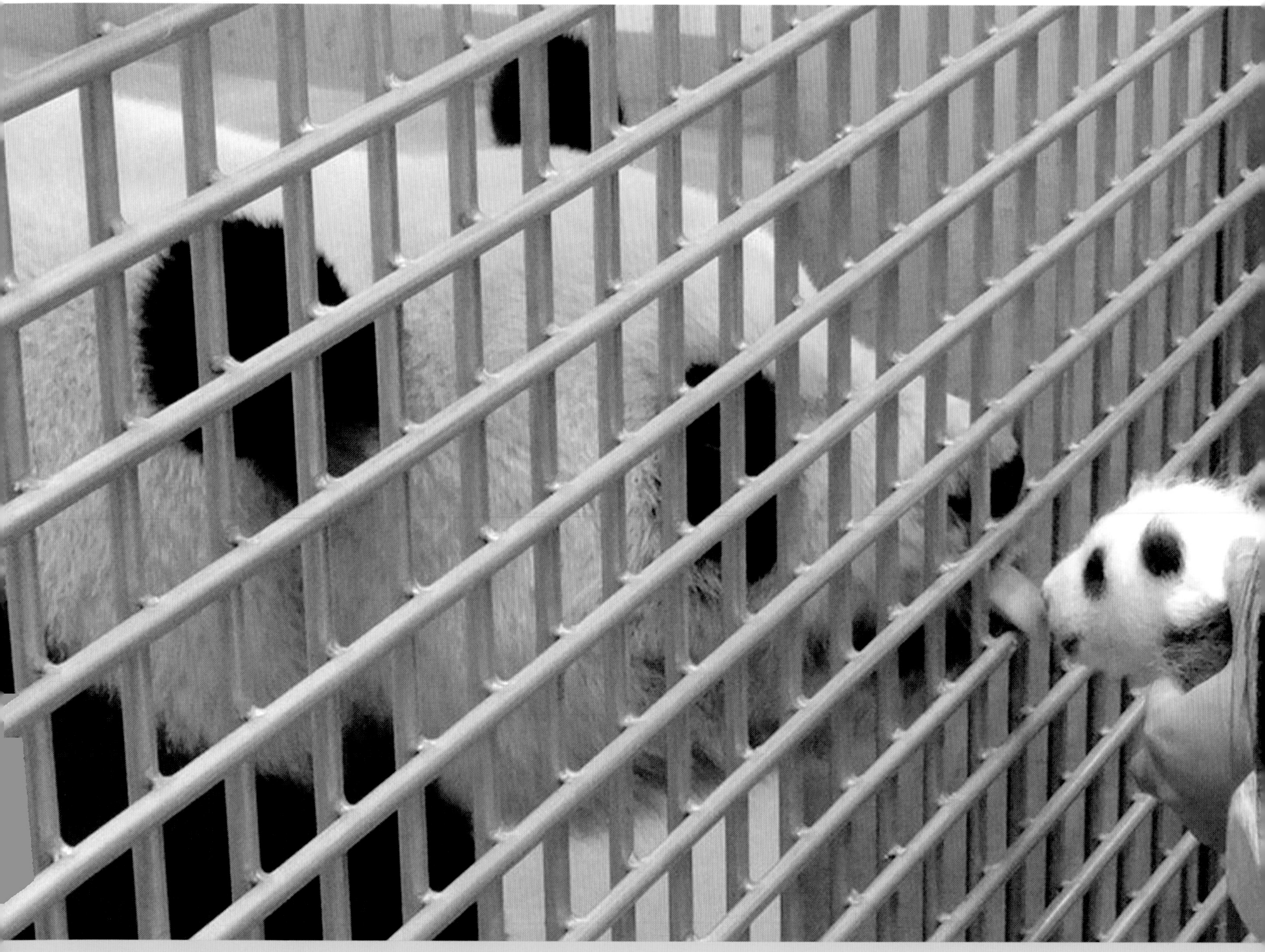

separated from her for one month.

After twice meeting through the rails, mother and daughter were finally reunited. When the rail was half-lifted, Yuan Yuan couldn't wait to bend down and slip underneath, holding her dear daughter in the mouth and hugging her. All the actions were quick and accurate. Perhaps Yuan Zai was accustomed to living in the baby nursing box where it could comfortably stretch its limbs, or lie on its back or belly. Therefore, Yuan Zai kept crying for the change. Yuan Yuan then constantly changed her ways of hugging for over one hour. Only when Yuan Zai found the nipple and began to suck did mother and daughter finally calm down.

Later, Yuan Yuan took care of Yuan Zai around the clock. Nannies had already understood the "language" of Yuan Zai: different cries had different meanings, including the desire to drink milk or feeling uncomfortable in mum's arms. Yuan Yuan and Yuan Zai would sleep head to back or back to back, or lie down in parallel. Mum might hold her daughter in her arms. Overall, they slept calmly and at ease. Yuan Yuan also invented a sleeping gesture, i.e., placing one leg on the rail, and moving her body by pushing the rails with her feet to avoid pressing her lovely daughter. Chen Yuyan said that Yuan Yuan was a good mother attentive and fond of learning. "It was a delight to see her

Yuan Zai, then two months old.

Yuan Zai, then six months old.

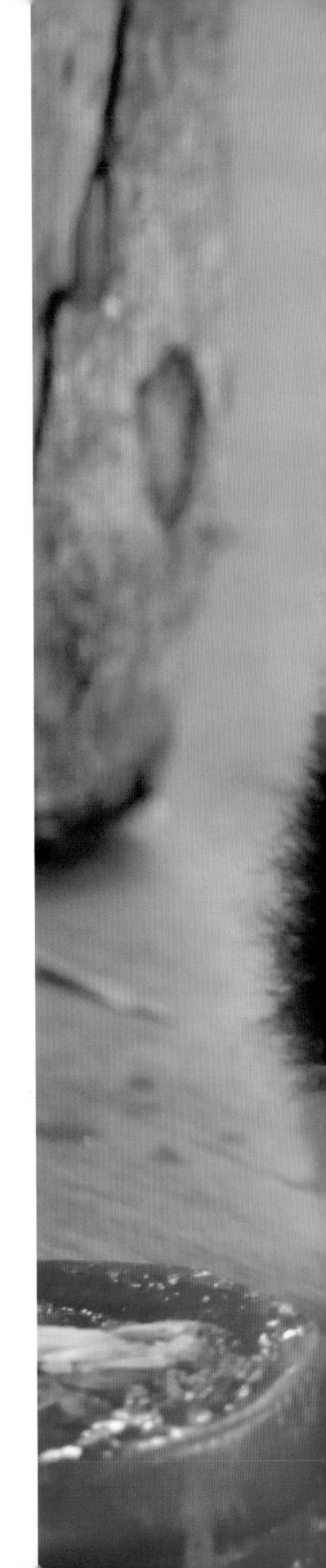

progress and it made me forget all the tiredness."

All the personnel accompanied the two pandas. Every second, they observed Yuan Yuan and Yuan Zai to ensure mother would not crush her daughter when extremely tired.

After the program on Yuan Zai returning to her mother was broadcast, lots of viewers shed silent tears. Soon, it was rebroadcast by the CBS in America, NHK in Japan and ATV in Singapore. The *Daily Telegraph* of the UK, the Russian news network and the press of South Korea also followed the news. More than two million people watched the show on the world famous video website YouTube.

On January 6, 2014, Yuan Zai began to meet the general public, who responded with delight to the "super lovely" pandas.

Birthday party for Yuan Zai in the Taipei Zoo on July 6, 2014.

PANDA LOVERS

Just like the rising sea tide, 8.5 million people log in the same website simultaneously; like selecting the most beautiful flower from all different species, 60 competitors will be selected from among the 60,000 applicants, then the number will be whittled down to 12 and then six.

On August 16, 2010, the worldwide activity of recruiting giant panda guardians hosted by the Chengdu Research Base of Giant Panda Breeding was initiated at the Shanghai World Expo. During the 100-day activity, all competitors fully showed their knowledge about pandas, their feelings towards pandas and their charming talent. Six competitors were selected as the first panda guardians, including Ali Shakorian of Sweden, Ashley Robertson of America, David Algranti of France, Huang Xi of the Chinese mainland, Wang Yuwen of Taiwan and Yumiko Kajiwara of Japan.

The worldwide activity of recruiting giant panda guardians is held every two years. Experts said that there are more than 100 million panda lovers in the world, including celebrities.

In October 1986, Britain's Queen Elizabeth II made a State visit to China. When her husband Prince Philip, chairman of the World Wildlife Fund (WWF), visiting the Wolong Giant Panda Protection Center, the first artificially-bred giant panda weighed 7.7 kilograms. The panda walked around him expecting a big hug. The prince said with a smile: "Go to find your mother, baby!" While looking at the blue sky after the rain, the prince gave the panda baby the name of "blue sky".

In September 2007, Bingxing and Huazuiba arrived at the Madrid Zoo in Spain. Queen Sophia opened the panda museum in person. In September 2010, Huazuiba gave birth to twins. On November 5, 2010, Queen Sophia visited the lovely twins and fed them personally.

On March 25, 2013, when the Chinese giant pandas Damao and Ermao arrived at the Toronto Pearson International Airport, Canadian Prime Minister Stephen Harper and his wife welcomed them in person while the Canadian national anthem played, just like welcoming the head of the state.

Wearing a cap with a panda design, Harper said it was a great honor to look after China's national treasures. "Their 10-year stay in Canada will remind us of the solid friendship between China and Canada and bring pleasure to all Canadians visiting the zoo".

When reporting the news, the Canadian Prime Minister's office pointed out that giant panda is considered as folk mascot in China, representing peace, friendship and fortune.

Panda guardian, Ashley from America, playing together with giant pandas.

Panda fans in various parts of the world.

For more than 20 years, China has carried out cooperation and research activities with such 16 zoos of 11 countries including the United States, Canada, Britain, Australia and Japan. More than 10 giant pandas living abroad were deeply loved by local people, especially those panda babies born in their country, so that birthday of each panda was celebrated in warm atmosphere.

On July 21, 1981, Ying Ying in Mexico gave birth to a panda baby named Duowei (child of Mexico). On its first birthday, Duowei got a one-meter-high cake, while on the Children's

On December 4, 2011, Tian Tian and Yang Guang reached Edinburgh in the United Kingdom. This marks the first time in 17 years giant pandas had landed in the United Kingdom.

On August 23, 2014, close to 20,000 people gathered to celebrate the one-year birthday of Bao Bao at the Washington National Zoo. Its parents Tian Tian and Mei Xiang came to the zoo in 2000.

Day, 2 million children celebrated the festival for Douwei. When the panda float passed through the streets, children sang the song for pandas.

On August 23, 2014, when Bao Bao in the Washington National Zoo turned one, the Chinese Embassy in the United States and the Washington National Zoo jointly celebrated the occasion.

In the early morning, many panda lovers and journalists rushed into the zoo to see Bao Bao, who, though sleeping when they arrived, soon posed for photographs and received the cheers of the crowd.

Bao Bao first chose the peach meaning the long life, then the bamboo meaning health and happiness, and last the pomegranate meaning having many children and fortune. After that, Bao Bao enjoyed the birthday dinner - the 20-kg ice cake composed of apple juice.

'SUPERSTAR'
OF THE UNITED STATES

On February 21, 1972, Premier Zhou Enlai greeted President Richard Nixon at the Beijing Capital International Airport, marking the first stage towards the formal establishment of Sino-US diplomatic relations.

All media focused attention on the Sino-US Summit meeting, while ignoring the activities of the American First Lady. In fact, she went to the Beijing Zoo to enjoy the pandas the day after arriving in China.

In 1953, Meilan in the Chicago Zoo died, and the panda house had since stayed empty for 18 years. Therefore, the action of the first lady indicated a silent appeal.

On February 25, President Nixon chaired a return banquet. The atmosphere was warm and friendly. President Nixon stood up to clink glasses with Marshal Ye Jianying. At that moment, Premier Zhou Enlai pushed a pack of cigarettes in front of President Nixon, and, pointing to the packet's panda logo, asked: "Do you like it?"

President Nixon did not understand the meaning at first, and answered: "Sorry, I don't smoke."

Premier Zhou again pointed at the panda pattern: "Do you like this? You gave us two musk oxen, and we plan to send you two pandas now in the Beijing Zoo."

Looking at Nixon talking with Marshal Ye, the first lady was so pleasantly surprised that she screamed: "Oh, my god! Dick! Dick! Did you hear what Primer Zhou said? Panda! Panda! He promises to send pandas to us. Our zoo will be packed with visitors!" Secretary of State William Rogers, Henry Kissinger and other senior officials all stood up. The first lady toasted to thank the Chinese Government and Premier Zhou Enlai.

Giant pandas in American zoo.

The scene was screened in the United States via live satellite, which aroused considerable interest of Americans. The *Washington Post* immediately commented that Zhou Enlai conquered the hearts of Americans through cute pandas. The media of the United States agreed that while 1972 was a year of recovering the Sino-US diplomatic relations, it could also be called "international panda year".

On April 16, 1972, Pandas Ling Ling and Xin Xin were moved to the United States by air.

When the two pandas reached the National Zoo in Washington, tens of thousands of people welcomed them despite rain. They were favored and loved by American people, and became the zoo's treasure. They attracted more than three million visitors every year, and appeared on front pages and covers of major American newspapers and journals many times.

A year after arriving at Washington DC, Ling Ling started oestrus, but Xin Xin was unresponsive. In the spring of 1983, however, after repeated training, Xin Xin and Ling Ling finally achieved natural mating.

However, the panda baby born in autumn only survived for three hours. For this reason, WWF headquarters in Switzerland issued a press release, and its flag flew at half-mast to express condolences.

It is the first time an international organization had done this to mark the death of a giant panda.

In the following several years, Ling Ling gave birth to four babies, but, regretfully, all died.

In 1992, 23-year-old Ling Ling died. When Xin Xin died in 1999, all Americans felt sad. State Department spokesman James Rubin specifically mentioned this at a news conference.

Although Xin Xin and Ling Ling had no baby in the United States, the Sino-US "panda exchanges" became more and more frequent and productive.

According to the provisions of the WWF and relevant international organizations, from the late 1980s, China began sending pandas to other countries for cooperative research instead of

American panda fans.

simply presenting as gifts.

Now, the zoos in Washington DC, San Diego, Atlanta and Memphis of the United States have charming giant pandas.

The panda icon was even used for metro tickets in Washington for a long time. The zoo gate is equipped with the landmark panda image, which shows the importance of pandas in the minds of Americans.

On July 9, 2005, Mei Xiang in the Washington Zoo gave birth to Tai Shan, who became an immediate favorite. When the announcement of its first meeting with the public was released online, some 13,000 tickets were sold in just two hours, so that the server crashed. Because too many people were eager to get tickets, ticket scalpers were able to sell them for US$75 apiece, and the zoo had to apologize to the public.

Tai Shan became a superstar. It succeeded in climbing trees for the first time following its mother's instructions. It even learned how to make snowballs. On its first birthday, it enjoyed apples, carrots, bamboo and ice cream cake. The breeder John Gibbon was accidentally injured by it in playing a "joke".... Tai Shan's every movement was reported.

One day at the age of four, it was napping while sitting, with its head burying low. Unexpectedly, it suddenly rolled forward on a lawn, which was photographed by a British

▼ October 17, 2005, a ceremony was held to name Tai Shan in Washington DC Zoo.

▲ Many came to see the elegant demeanor of Tai Shan.

160

On February 4, 2010, American born Tai Shan was about to leave for Chengdu. People came to see the panda off.

On March 9, 2010, Tai Shan showed off in the Sichuan Ya'an Bifengxia Base.

woman. It became another piece of news.

On February 4, 2010, Tai Shan had to be returned to China according to the agreement, and tens of thousands of Americans bid farewell at the zoo despite snow. A young man made a marriage proposal to his girlfriend in front of the panda house, arousing cheers and laughter.

Extremely popular Tai Shan now lives in the Bifengxia Panda Base of CRCCGP, together with many other "returnees". American panda fans visit it from time to time. Maybe the familiar English greetings will make it think of the beautiful days in the Washington Zoo.

Today, the superstar Bao Bao in the Washington Zoo even outshines Tai Shan. Bao Bao is a daughter of Mei Xiang, and its name was determined by 123,000 fans worldwide. On the 100th day after birth, it was officially named Bao Bao. Madame Peng Liyuan, wife of President Xi Jinping, and President Barack Obama's wife Michelle, released videos of congratulations.

The Panda Exhibition Hall in the Washington Zoo has a small showroom exhibiting cultural relics of pandas. Some projects also attract visitor participation. By clicking the mouse in front of the panda genealogy panel, you can know the parents or children of a panda.

Many visitors want to hug and touch pandas. In fact, there is a small piece of genuine panda fur in the display panel. Careful tourists can touch it personally.

◀ Tai Shan and Mother Mei Xiang.

▶ On January 6, 2014, giant panda Bao Bao made its debut before the press in Washington Zoo.

FROM 'WAIF' TO MESSENGER OF THE OLYMPIC GAMES

In 1983, bashania fangiana in the Minshan Mountain and Qionglai Mountain, the main origins of giant pandas, blossomed and died. Like rice, bashania fangiana is a graminaceous plant and its growth period is 30-50 years. That is to say, at the end of each life cycle, they will die and sow seeds, and bamboo forests will formed again years later. As bashania fangiana is the staple food of pandas, its blooming means pandas' great famine.

Chengguan Town, Baoxing County, Sichuan Province, is far from the core area of native forests where giant pandas live. On one occasion, four local people went to Qingxi to gather wild vegetables. They worked while laughing.

Yin Haicheng first noticed that a black and white object was moving on a tree some 40 meters away. "Look, look, a giant panda!"

They rushed towards the tree, and helped the wandering panda get down.

The poor panda had sparse fur because of malnutrition, and was trembling because of fright. They immediately fed it with a corn pancake. After sniffing, it ate part of it.

They were happy. They put it into a jute bag with four large holes for ventilation, and went downhill.

◀ 2008 Beijing Olympic mascot Fuwa.

Yin Haicheng fed it with sugared and delicious corn porridge in his home. Three days later, it became vigorous and accustomed to the life there. Yin Haicheng put it in a bamboo basket, and took it to the authorities of the Fengtongzhai National Nature Reserve. When people there asked him about its name, Yin Haicheng said that he had not named it. Someone suggested naming it as Yinyin because it was discovered by Yin Haicheng and Yin Haiyun.

As Sichuan people cannot distinguish "yin" from "yong", local journalists mistakenly wrote "Yong Yong", which was the origin of its name.

In March 1982, President Armand Hammer of the Occidental Petroleum Corporation of the United States visited China. When meeting with Deng Xiaoping, he request to borrow a pair of giant pandas for the Los Angeles Olympics in 1984. Deng Xiaoping thought it was creative, and agreed to let the relevant departments study and handle this issue.

The China Wildlife Conservation Association solicited the advice of relevant experts about which giant pandas should be chosen.

◁ In July 2001, giant pandas made a special trip to Moscow in support of China's bid to host the 2008 Olympic Games.

After over half a year of recovery, Yong Yong living a comfortable life had become a handsome "guy" good at many skills including somersault, swinging, apple grabbing, climbing and wrestling, etc. Experts liked the cute Yong Yong at first sight.

In July 1984, on the eve of the opening ceremony of the 23rd Olympic Games, Yong Yong and Ying Ying, upon the instruction of Deng Xiaoping, were moved to Los Angeles as scheduled. Hammer personally greeted the pandas at the airport.

During the Olympic Games, Yong Yong and Ying Ying attracted 2 million people. The media called them as "honorable messengers" and "guests of Sam the Eagle". Pandas made the Los Angeles Olympics more delightful and enthusiastic than any previous one.

After the Los Angeles Olympics, upon invitation of Mayor Dianne Feinstein of San Francisco, Yong Yong and Ying Ying were moved to the San Francisco Zoo. To enable more people to see them, the zoo required each visitor could stay in front of the handrail for only three minutes. To get the valuable opportunity, people had to wait for three or four hours to buy tickets. In successive four weeks of display in San Francisco, about 1.5 million visitors were received.

On the evening of November 11, 2005, children in Chengdu cheered for the successful choice of giant pandas as the 2008 Beijing Olympic Games mascot.

FINAL WISH OF A
BRITISH OLD MAN

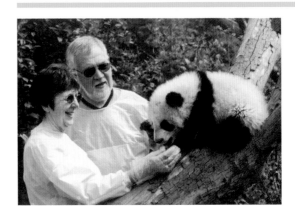

One day in 2003, a British old man named David Tena was lying on a hospital bed after brain tumor surgery. He had very bad moods. To make him happy, his wife read the newspaper to him. That day, the *Daily Mail* reported new achievements of artificially breeding pandas in the Chengdu Research Base of Giant Panda Breeding. Panda babies in the photos were so cute that the old man laughed. He was a great fan, having seen giant pandas Ming and Chi Chi in his childhood.

After an unprecedented bloody battle before Christmas in 1944, the World War II was coming to an end with allied victory. Just at that moment when British people prepared to celebrate, the London Zoo announced the death of giant panda Ming. *The Times* published important articles to express condolences.

Why did the British have such deep feelings upon Ming?

◁ British couple happy with the giant panda.

171

In fact, when Nazi Germany launched air raids against London, Ming was optimistic and behaved as usual despite alarms and deafening explosions from time to time. BBC and military media of the United States specially filmed anti-Nazi documentaries in which Ming was the leading actor, and continuously reported the "British people still have high morale". British citizens saw the giant panda as a steadfast and optimistic anti-fascist fighter.

In the 1950s, Chi Chi also left an unforgettable impression to British people.

At that time, an old couple vowed to go to China to see the cute pandas.

Strangely, the dying old man, with a desire to see the pandas in China, began recovering. Five months later, the old couple flew from London to Chengdu. Zhang Zhihe, director of the Chengdu Panda Base, showed them around.

In the panda kindergarten, one panda baby named Ya Xing hugged the legs of the old man, making him laugh. When he picked it up, it unexpectedly kissed him, which made him so happy. He kept pinching himself and asked: "It's true! Pandas are really the world's most fascinating animals! "

Following the failed marriage of Chi Chi and An An, another between Jia Jia from the United Kingdom and Ling Ling from the United States followed suit in 1981. Because of ignorance about pandas' aesthetics and conditions, many failed "forced marriages" occurred.

Every year when the primula malacoides bloom, adult pandas start oestrus. They will apply their secretions to the tree trunks, sending out strong signals of love. For mating, male pandas will participate in a fierce and brutal "contest", while female pandas only "watch" and try to stir up the combatants to make the fighting more exciting. Love only belongs to strong and mighty winners.

Mating of Giant Pandas

In the wild, female giant pandas begin to go on heat at the age of 6.5 years and could become pregnant a year later. This is two or three years earlier than captive female pandas. The female giant pandas can reproduce for 13 years. However, the male giant pandas become mature enough to have reproductive ability only after 16 years, and will lose their mating ability when at about the age of 21. Giant pandas' estrus time is in spring, from late March to mid-May, and mostly in April, when Primula malacoides are in blossom. Some giant pandas mate in January and also in September. The Estrous cycle happens once every two years, and giant pandas generally calve in autumn. In the case when a panda cub dies prematurely, the mother would be on heat in spring the following year.

In February 1963, the East and the West were still continuing the cold war. For the "transnational marriage" of a pair of pandas, British zoology doctor Desmond Morris left London for Moscow by air.

The bride was the giant panda Chi Chi, star of the London Zoo, and one of the favorite animals of British children. An Austrian merchant obtained her after several years of efforts. In return, he presented the Beijing Zoo with three giraffes, two rhinos, two hippos and two zebras. He had planned to transport Chi Chi to the United States for sale at a good price, but failed. He had to start a European tour exhibition of Chi Chi. It proved a great hit in England as crowds flocked to London Zoo, where Chi Chi finally settled in 1958.

In 1960, Chi Chi started oestrus. London Zoo hastily prepared for a mating. At that time, An An was in the prime of life in the Moscow Zoo. However, it took three years of negotiations to reach consensus. Dr. Desmond Morris thought it funny because their dispute was about the ownership of the panda baby. To him, it seemed wrong to "count your chickens before they hatch," as the old saying goes. However, a compromise plan acceptable by both sides was finally decided.

◁ Giant panda Chi Chi walking on the stone wall in London.

◁ Looking for love.

In March 1963, Chi Chi finally arrived in Moscow by air for mating with An An. Maybe due to the influence of the Cold War between East and West, the two pandas coldly stared at each other and showed their teeth as they prowled around. Finally, they began to fight, and breeders had to separate them.

In order to let Chi Chi adapt to the proposed bridegroom and the new environment, the United Kingdom agreed to let Chi Chi stay there. In autumn, staff from the London Zoo flew to Moscow, and put Chi Chi and An An in the same cage again.

Zoologists opened eyes wide. To prevent accidents, wooden shields, a water hose and tranquilizer guns were prepared. Enthusiastic An An barked and chased Chi Chi, intending to hug Chi Chi. But Chi Chi, like a British noble, remained aloof and even roared when An An approached. An An soon lost its limited patience and sat dejectedly beside the wall while panting.

Night fell. Zoologists wishfully looked forward to the mating of Chi Chi and An An. They observed all night, but got nothing but the snoring of the two pandas. Early in the morning, energetic An An attacked once again. It climbed onto Chi Chi's back and grabbed her neck. Although Chi Chi did not protest strongly, it covered its privates with its thick and fat tail, making An An suffer defeat while seemingly on the verge of victory.

Nobody wanted to give up. On September 11, 1968, An An was taken to London from Moscow. Zoologists injected love potions into Chi Chi, while arranging for An An to stay until May the following year. Ultimately, however, this international "forced marriage" ended in failure.

Waiting for its lover to come onto the tree.

In 1966, the giant panda Chi Chi returns to London after a mating failure in Moscow.

'Chi-Chi' Moscow to London

CARGO

BEA

A male panda hitting the road to look for love.

Tormented by sexual desire, a male panda rubs its body on a tree trunk to attract a female.

VIDEO

Vie for camera show

The 14-year-old virgin Chi Chi died in solitude in the summer of 1974. Three months later, the old bachelor An An died, too. Arranged marriages often cause tragedies and this was one such case in the panda world.

Panda's aesthetics is entirely different from that of humans. We think that chubby male pandas with round faces are handsome. But females often favor unattractive and even ugly males. Perhaps Chi Chi did not like An An's appearance. So no matter how hard An An tried, Chi Chi would not accept.

But Lord Scott of the United Kingdom once saw Chi Chi in London, and it left a memorable impression. In 1961, the World Wide Fund for Nature (WWF) was established, and the panda pattern elaborately designed by Scott according Chi Chi's image was unanimously adopted as its logo. Although this happened in the Cold War era, indicating Chinese pandas transcended ideology and were recognized as beautiful by the whole world.

FAILURE OF 'FORCED MARRIAGE'